CRESWELL AND ITS MINE

Barry Vardy

MINERVA PRESS

LONDON
ATLANTA MONTREUX SYDNEY

ISBN 0 75410 079 0

First Published 1998 by
MINERVA PRESS
195 Knightsbridge
London SW7 1RE

Printed in Great Britain for Minerva Press

CRESWELL AND
ITS MINE

Some, but not all, of the stories based on the Saul family –
my mother's family – are fiction. However they are all
based on true happenings in Creswell.

Where I thought any problems might occur in using real
names in the book, I have changed the names of the
characters concerned.

My grateful thanks to all the people – too numerous to mention – who have provided me with information about the village and mine. But a special thank-you to my brother Alan and sister Jane. Without their help the book would never have been written.

Contents

Part One

The Beginning

Prologue	September 1998 (First)	11
One	A New Mine and Village	13
Two	A New Life	21

Part Two

The Prosperous Years

Three	First Aid: Small and Large	39
Four	Village Entertainment	52
Five	Snow White, the Big Porky	65
Six	Mabel and the First World War	78

Part Three

Hard Times

Seven	After the First World War	93
Eight	The Miners Locked Out	107
Nine	The Recovery	120
Ten	The General Strike	134

Part Four

The Changing Years

Eleven	Joe's Shops	151
Twelve	Margaret's Wedding	165
Thirteen	Creswell's Cinema	178
Fourteen	The Second World War	190

Part Five

The Disaster

Fifteen	The Fire	205
Sixteen	The Aftermath	219
Epilogue	September 1998 (Last)	227

Part One

The Beginning

September 1998 (First)

Two boys were playing football in a disused pit yard in the old mining village of Creswell when they noticed in the distance an old man walking with a limp at the side of a small pit pony. His head was bowed low and he was talking quietly to the animal. The boys walked slowly up to the stooped figure but he did not turn his head.

One of the lads put his hand on the neck of the pony and started to stroke its coat. 'What is its name?' asked the boy very quietly.

''Is name is 'Ector,' replied the old man, 'and I am John Saul.' Pointing across to the pit yard, he said, 'We worked in the mine that was in that area over there, all our lives. But now it's all gone and no one would ever know it had ever been there.'

'We have come with our mother to the village,' said one of the boys. 'She is visiting a friend in one of those houses.' The lads pointed to the model village. 'But we did not know anything about the mine. We didn't even know that one ever existed.'

'Well,' said John, 'if you have an 'our ter spare and yer mam knows weer yer are, I'll tell yer the whole story.'

The lads sat on a seat at the side of the old cricket ground. John sat on the concrete at the side of the overgrown grass and started to talk.

Chapter One
A New Mine and Village

On a fine spring day in 1895 Emerson Muschamp Bainbridge stood on a lush grass field between the village of Elmton and the hamlet of Creswell on the Derbyshire county border with Nottingham. He was a tall thickset man in his early fifties, with a round face, dark brown eyes covered by light rimmed spectacles, a sweeping moustache, and thinning hair which was covered by a dark trilby. He was wearing a dark three-piece suit and shiny black leather boots.

He closed his eyes and allowed himself to reminisce back through his early life of education and work in industry. Educated at Doncaster, he was later articled to mining engineering with the Marquis of Londonderry and studied at Durham University. He was the manager of the Tinsley collieries in the 1870s, and later for the Duke of Norfolk's Nunnery mines. In 1879 he became chairman of the New Hucknell colliery. He was also a director for several railway companies.

However, he was here today in this small hamlet of around thirty to forty homes with a population of less than one hundred people, containing several farms, two public houses, a wheelwright and two shopkeepers. The point of his visit was to meet two important men: the Duke of Portland, the owner of the land; and John Houfton, his present company manager, to discuss the sinking of the mine.

The Duke arrived first, his horse-drawn carriage having travelled round the bumpy road from Welbeck House, through the Crags where some of the first Stone Age men had lived over ten thousand years earlier, and past the fields full of wheat, barley, oats and a variety root of vegetables. He was a man of medium height, fair hair, blue eyes and a broad clean-shaven face, wearing a heavy horsehair overcoat and knee-high leather, laced boots.

The Duke of Portland had inherited the Duchy of Norfolk when his father died in 1879. The two men had known each other well from the early 1870s when Bainbridge was a director for the Midland Railway Company that had laid tracks through the Duke's land; and in 1889 when Emerson had negotiated the lease to mine the Top-Hard seam of coal under land owned by the Portlands within the parishes of Bolsover, Elmton, Derbyshire and other sites. The new company was The Bolsover Colliery Company, and Creswell was their second mine.

Emerson was also pleased to have obtained the services of Sir Henry Hall Scott as the first chairman of his new company. Sir Henry was later to take a distinguished part in the Boer War in South Africa. He was the captain of the flagship *Good Hope*.

The Duke alighted from his carriage. He held out his hand and said, 'Good morning, Bainbridge! A lovely morning!'

Emerson shook the Duke's hand.

'Good morning, sir, indeed it is!' Both men turned round at the sound of a horse's hooves to see the arrival of John Houfton from a westerly direction.

Climbing from his horse, Houfton inclined his head.

'Good morning to you, gentlemen. I am sorry I am late, I was detained at Bolsover.'

'Good morning,' replied both men together.

'I trust that there was no problem on your journey here,' added the Duke.

'No, no!' replied the manager. 'I enjoy riding; it gives me a break from my duties.'

Houfton was a tall, slim man; his bald head was covered by a riding cap. He had a grey curling moustache and dark rimmed glasses covered his light blue eyes. He was wearing a black leather jacket, tight-fitting riding trousers and knee-high leather riding boots.

'To business,' said Bainbridge. 'His lordship is wondering about the viability of the mine on this site, and especially the effect it may have on the Crags.'

'Well!' said John, thoughtfully. 'When we sank Bolsover in '90, no one thought the pit would be viable, but two years later we have a daily output of two thousand tons. I know that other people do not agree, but I believe that there will be coal under there,' he pointed to the ground, 'in the same way that there is at Bolsover. If I had not thought so I would not have produced the plans last year. The mine will not be near enough to the Crags to have any effect on their structures.'

This pleased the Duke, who would receive sixpence for every ton of coal that the mine produced.

On 25th February, 1896 John Houfton cabled a message to Bainbridge at the House of Commons – he was at that time the Member of Parliament for Gainsbourgh – saying that the Top-Hard coal seam at Creswell had been reached by the No. 1 shaft.

The seam was four hundred and forty-five yards deep, and it was six inches thicker than the one at Bolsover. By

March 1896 it was estimated that fifty thousand tons of coal could be obtained that year.

The No. 2 shaft reached the Top-Hard seam about two weeks later. A mine must have two shafts – sometimes two sloping tunnels – which connect the surface with the underground. Not only do the shafts transport men and material, but they are very important for ventilation. The air goes down the mine by one shaft and returns to the surface by the other. This prevents many accidents involving noxious and flammable gases, for example, firedamp or methane gas. The ventilation also removes the problem of heat in deep mines by extracting the hot air and much of the dust that is produced in the colliery.

Coal turning began in this modern mine in April 1897. Two railway companies had sidings into the colliery. The colliery produce was also utilised for coke, steam raising, gas and domestic purposes. The pit head and pit bottom underground were lit by electricity, and the miners all had their safety lamps lit by electricity in the lamp cabin. The shafts were powered by steam winding engines.

Bainbridge was a religious man who believed in the welfare of his men and their families. He secured a ten acre tract of land from the Duke of Portland near the mine, and erected cottages for his employees. Percy Houfton, the general manager's brother, was engaged as the architect for a modern idea to build a model village for the mine workers, similar to a smaller version of fifty homes built earlier in Bolsover. Creswell's model consisted of two hundred and eighty two-storied cottages, in four to eight blocks, containing five or six rooms, in the shape of a double octagon, with an inner and outer circle. A Co-operative Society, an Institute and a cricket ground were also included in the plans.

★

Jack Dakin had lived in Creswell all his life. Like his father before him he had worked on George Bakewell's farm since he was thirteen. He was six feet tall, with broad shoulders and a strong muscular body. His dark, tight curly hair, blue eyes and pale complexion helped to enhance his stature. After ten years on the farm, he was showing his young wife Rose – who was carrying their six-month-old son John in her arms – one of the new rented cottages in the model village that had cost the mine owners two hundred pounds each to build. They were both very excited; for the first eighteen months of their married life they had lived with their in-laws. This was their first home, and it was available because Jack had started to work in the mine.

It was 1899, John was looking forward to the work, but he hoped that the strike that occurred two years earlier when the Creswell men asked to be paid on a daily basis, rather then by tonnage rates, would not happen again. Bainbridge had argued that the company could not offer more then 1s 4d a ton; but the men went on strike until they received 1s 5½d, the same wages as the miners at Bolsover. That was now behind them. John was pleased that he was not involved.

Rose was a small plump woman, looking older then her twenty years, with light, short cut hair, grey eyes, and a full face. The colliery owners had rented them a cottage on the inner circle of the model. The upstairs of their home had one large bedroom at the front of the house and two small ones at the back. The bedroom at the front of the cottage had a wooden fitted wardrobe and a small fire grate; the two smaller rooms at the rear also contained fire grates, with windows overlooking the backyard.

The ground floor had a front room with a fire grate and a wooden storage cupboard. The living room had a coal fire and cooking range combined. In front of the window was a brown pot sink, and in the corner a space was left for an iron copper to heat the water for washing and bathing. The back door went out into an asphalt backyard. At the bottom of the yard were outbuildings containing a dry toilet, storage space and coalhouse.

'They empty them loos every week,' said Jack. 'They bring tubs down the railway line that runs down the road between the two terraces. And that's 'ow the coal ull come from the pit when it's delivered. We get a load er coal every month yer know, as part er the wages,' he said.

Rose turned to her husband, smiled and replied, 'No moor choppin' wood, eh, Jack.'

'That's not all!' said her husband and inclined his head. 'The 'ouse is lit up by that fancy electricity that comes from the pit; no gas or paraffin lamps. We have ter fetch the watter from the well at Fox Green; yer got ter go over a wooden bridge that's over the railway line.'

Rose went back into the house, entered the front room and looked out of the window. She loved this scene. Outside their front door was a small flower garden, surrounded by a wooden fence. Overlooking the garden was a large green with over two hundred yards of footpath, which was surrounded by the cottages. There was a road running between the top and bottom half of the model village; and one between the rows of cottages. A bandstand, several rustic seats, and a special children's play area were also on the green.

'Yer can join the band and blow yer own trumpet – they say that Mr Hind is a good band leader,' Rose said laughing.

'Yes! And the babbies, includin' the one that's on its way,' said Jack pointing his finger a Rose's stomach, ''ave a smashin' play area. There's the Co-op were yer get yearly dividend; there's plenty er 'awkers comin' round as well, on their bikes. We can still get milk, eggs and butter from Dad at the farm. There's a library in the Institute, and I can even learn ter play cricket.' He picked up a piece of wood and demonstrated an extravagant off-drive.

'What about an allotment?' suggested Rose. 'We could grow our own veg, and save money.'

'That would be a good idea.' Jack inclined his head and smiled. 'They're only four bob a year, and yer can put flowers in the front gardin' and win first prize in the 'orticultural show. I can imagine them tulips, pinks, primulas, daffs, foxgloves, forget-me-nots, pansies, marigolds and all them other varieties of flowers that will be in bloom all year round in that front garden!'

Rose's heart was full of joy. 'On Sundays we can go fer walks inter Sullivan's wood. It's only just over that railway line from 'ere,' she said, pointing in a westerly direction. 'It's a lovely wood, yer get cowslips, daisies, catkins, anemones, fern, bluebells and all sorts out of there. And in September we can go blackberryin' and make some jam.'

'Somethin' yer didn't know,' replied Jack. 'The colliery pay for a day trip ter Blackpool ev'ry year, *and* they 'ave also bought a site at a seaside place in Wales called Rhyl, where we can go for a week in summer next year.'

'Somethin' else,' continued Jack. 'The colliery pay for a full-time bobby, so there wont be much trouble. There's also a full-time nurse, but the Duchess of Portland pays 'er wages. She could be useful when the next un arrives.'

'It seems too good ter be true,' said Rose, 'let's go an' sit on one of them seats in the sun and get sunburned.' Rose held her hand out to her husband feeling that this was one of the happiest days of her life.

Six months later Rose presented Jack with another son, Percy; their joy was complete and they thanked God for their good fortune.

Jack came home from work one day at the end of June 1900; Rose was very distressed.

'What's up?' asked Jack.

'Will yer go and ask the nurse ter come and look at the two boys?' Rose asked her husband.

When the nurse arrived she told Jack to go into the village and ask the doctor to call.

'These boys are running a very high temperature.' She spoke with concern. The doctor came; but nothing could be done. Both boys died within four days of each other, in the middle of July, from fever. The Dakins were in despair. Over a period of twelve months, sixty-three people died in the village of the epidemic; fifty-six were children under the age of one year.

The Dakins had more children in later years; but the mental scars from the loss of their first two children remained for a long time. This was only the first of several tragedies that was to hit the very close mining community over the next fifty years; but there were also many good times to help to compensate for their difficulties.

Chapter Two

A New Life

John Saul sat on a wooden chair in front of a wooden table in the kitchen of his home, with a ceramic pint pot of tea in front of him. He was a small thin man with fair hair, blue eyes and a light moustache. He wore a collarless cream striped shirt, and baggy trousers; he was tying the laces on his black leather hobnailed boots. His wife had just woken him to say that his breakfast was ready. Mary Saul placed her husband's breakfast in front of him on the table; his plate was full of bacon, eggs and black pudding. Mary sat at the other side of the table and cut herself a thick slice of bread from a home-made loaf, buttered it, and topped it with home-made marmalade.

'It is strange ter think that this will be our last meal in this 'ouse,' Mary sighed.

John inclined his head. 'Well!' he exclaimed. 'I was born in this 'ouse; we've spent the first five years of our married life 'ere, an' today will be our last. I have loved this old house, but terday we must go to the new village and work for the colliery.'

'We'll finish breakfast an' I'll wake the two babbies and feed 'em before we start and put the furniture inter the wagon,' said Mary. She stood up and went out of the room.

John went outside and looked at the old Elizabethan house with its gabled front where his family had lived in

Doncaster, on the same farm, for over four hundred years. When John's father died the previous year, he had left many debts and now everything had to be sold to clear them. What was very sad for John was selling the animals, particularly the horses, although he would still be working with ponies in the mine. He remembered with joy the many hunts that he had been involved in. It had been a boast of his father that his oldest son could ride a horse at the age of three; but now they were all gone except one old dray horse that would pull the cart with his family and furniture to their new home.

John went back into the house to see his four-year-old daughter Ellen, and two-year-old son Joe sat at the table eating their breakfast out of a wooden bowl containing porridge covered with treacle and warm milk.

The children were excited. 'When are we goin', Dad?' asked Ellen.

'When we've put the furniture onter the wagon and you've eaten yer porridge,' said John, and pointed to her bowl.

'Joe don't want ter go, Dad,' screeched Ellen. ''E wants ter stay on the farm with the 'osses!'

'Well! 'E's not got much choice,' replied John and turned towards the two children. 'Firstly, all the 'osses apart from Sam, the old dray, went last night, and secondly, 'e can't stay 'ere by 'imself.'

Mary walked back into the room and tapped her daughter on the knuckles. 'Don't tell tales, young lady, you'd get an angel 'ung fer nothin',' she warned.

'It's true, Mam!' the young girl replied. ''E told me that last night when we was in bed.'

'All right, stop talkin' and finish yer breakfast, every time yer talk yer miss a bite,' said her mother. She poked her face into her daughter's face and smiled.

Mary was also sorry to be leaving the area. She was a slim, attractive woman, five feet four inches tall, with fair hair, brown eyes and rosy cheeks. Her parents were of Irish descent, tinkers by trade; before her marriage she had spent her life living in a caravan, travelling to sell their wares. She met John at one of the tinker's fairs in Doncaster, when his father was selling horses. They had married at St Peter's in Chains Catholic Church in the town over five years ago, and this had been their home ever since – her first real home. It was the only stable life she had known; now, they were going to a new village, a different type of people, and a complete change in her family's life.

John stacked the furniture on the wagon and fastened it down with rope. He hitched the horse to the wheeled vehicle, lifted his family on to the wagon, then climbed on and sat next to his wife. He took one last look back at the old house – he had a tear in his eye – before setting of on the two-day journey through Bawtry and Worksop to Creswell.

'Gee-up,' he told the old horse, with a dry mouth and a touch of sadness in his heart.

It was autumn of 1902 that the Saul family went to live in their new village. The mine had been in existence for six years. The model village was completed. A new church was built by the Duke of Portland in 1899. A Wesleyen congregation had meetings in the colliery Institute, and the UMFC had built a new chapel on the main street; however, John knew that there was not yet a Catholic congregation, but he hoped that this could be arranged.

A large new school had been built with contributions from the colliery company and the Duke of Portland. The infants' school had been there for twenty-five years; however it was in the process of renovation. Football and cricket teams, a Brass Band, an Orchestral Society, and a Boys' Brigade had already been formed in the village. John knew there were allotments to rent, and this would be one of his first priorities. He still loved working on the land, and could provide his family with a variety of fresh fruit and vegetables.

There were two railway stations in Creswell. The one at the top of the village was built in the late 1890s by the Lancashire, Derbyshire, and East Coast (LD & EC) Railway Company. The line travelled from Langwith in the south-west to Chesterfield and Sheffield in the north. This was part of a planned railway link to run between Warrington and Sutton-on-Sea (east to west across England), visualising the expansion of trade in exported coal to the continent; but for the time being, the project had run out of money when the line had reached Lincoln.

Emerson Bainbridge was a director of both railway companies with lines running through the village.

The station in the middle of the village was owned by the Midland Railway Co. Their trains had delivered the first passengers to the village in 1875. The line went from Nottingham in the south to Worksop in the north-east. The railways were important to the colliery. Not only did they transport the coal, but they were a major form of daily travel for many of the one thousand four hundred men and boys who worked at the mine.

John drove his horse and cart into the village. A new housing estate was in the process of creation at the side and back of the church. The land was owned by the Duke of

Portland which was let by the solicitors, Cook, Hofton and Johnson. The solicitors sub-let the land on a ninety year lease to the builders. John took the turning to the left and entered the new estate to find the family's new home at 45 Duchess Street.

The street was busy; builders were still working at the end of the road, which consisted of two blocks of terraced houses. John lifted his family off the wagon, and unhitched the horse. He gave the horse a drink – the animal was sweating after the long journey – and led him on to a grass field across from their home.

The front door of their new home opened directly onto the street. Entering the front door they found another door to the left which lead to a staircase going upstairs. The first floor consisted of a large bedroom at the front of the house, and two smaller bedrooms at the rear. All three rooms contained a small fire grate, with wooden floors and, the front bedroom had a large wooden fitted cupboard.

The ground rooms had cement floors. There was a large room at the front containing a fire grate. A room at the rear with wooden fitted cupboards and drawers, and a large black leaded fire grate with a combined cooking range. Attached at the rear was a small kitchen or scullery containing a brown oblong sink and a large copper for heating the water. The lighting was by electricity generated by the mine. The backyard was asphalted, with outbuildings at the end of the yard containing a dry toilet, coalhouse and a storage shed.

John and Mary removed the furniture from the wagon, with the assistance of the excited children.

'We get the watter from Fox Green, Mary,' John said, pointing his arm, 'it's just over the field.'

'Yes,' said Mary and turned to her husband, 'and I see there's a big field at the back of Duke Street – the street we just drove the cart up – fer the kids ter play on.'

'They call that the rec,' replied John. He turned round and looked the other way and pointed. 'Yer see just over there, they call them the Crags. They are limestone rocks with caves in 'em. They reckoned that men lived in 'em over ten thousand years ago. They reckon there's some pictures painted on the walls er caves.'

'That's incredible!' Mary looked surprised as she spoke. 'I wonder if they'll remember us in ten thousand years time?'

'I don't know, but a don't think we'll be here ter find out,' laughed John.

★

John went to work at the mine for the first time the following Monday. He was slightly apprehensive. Although he was to be the ostler foreman over the men and boys who worked the pit ponies and most of his work was on the pit top in the yard, he still had to go down the mine every day to ensure the welfare of the animals.

The pit ponies were kept in their own stable in the mine underground. They were brought to the surface for two weeks every year during the annual holidays in the summer. A lad of about fourteen years of age, who had been an apprentice on the pit top for a year, was responsible for his own pony. He would take the animal to the coalface, hitch him to an empty tub and deliver it to the area where the miners were extracting coal. The pony was then unhitched from the tub. The men worked in small groups and were employed by overseers called butties.

Miners used picks, hammers and ringers to get the coal. Props and bars were placed in rows to support the roof where the mineral had been extracted. The colliers filled the tubs with forks to avoid excess slack in the tubs. When the tub was full it was pushed down a sloping railway line. The coal was delivered to the pit bottom by a haulage system, and removed from the mine by the shaft. At the end of the day, the lad took his pony back to his stable, rubbed him down, fed, watered, and bedded the pony down with clean straw, and checked the animal's overall condition.

On the surface the tubs were passed into screens where the coal from the tubs were tipped and sorted into different sizes. Much of the slack was sold to the Lancashire steel mills. The small coal of about ½" went for steam raising, including many of the railway companies. Lumps of around 2" went for gas production. The next size was for various industrial purposes depending on customer requirements. Larger nuts 4" by 2½" were popular for household usage in London. Cobbles of 8" by 4" were utilised by hotels, hospitals and, in the fishing season, trawlers.

The coal mined at Creswell had the advantage of having less than half a per cent sulphur which was ideal for blast furnaces, in, for example, the Sheffield steelworks. Many exporters required lumps over 8" by 4". The War Office also utilised the large size coal for annealing the big guns. Various sizes went for home burning. The small coal went to a washery where it was cleaned and sized again.

In the early years coal was exported from Creswell to Russia, Norway, Sweden, Denmark, Italy, Germany and Holland; via Immingham and Grimsby docks.

The colliery at that time was one of the most prosperous in the country. Over three thousand tons of coal was mined every day, and the inhabitants in the village were over four thousand.

Two items of interest that John had learnt on his first day at work. The owners had proposed a pension scheme for the men, whereby if the miners subscribed a penny a week, the owners would put in ½d. And there was going to be books for loan from the Institute library. Both John and Mary could read, and the ostler still longed for the leather-backed volumes that they had back on the farm. There were book titles by authors such as the Brontës, Wilkie Collins, Tennyson, Anthony Trollope and George Eliot.

★

October 11th, 1902 was Joe's second birthday. Mary decided to have a party for him, and invite five or six small children from the street. It could also be a house-warming gathering for her new neighbours. Ellen met her father on his way home from work at the bottom of the green iron bridge; the bridge was the footpath over the railway from the colliery yard on to Morven Street.

'Yer look excited young lady,' said John, and smiled as he took hold of the small girl's hand.

'Mam's made some jelly and trifle, and there's some new bread and buns, Dad. She's iced a cake and put two candles on it!' said his daughter.

''Ave the other kids from the street come yet, or is it a bit early?' enquired John.

'Vicky from next door's come, but there's another four more ter turn up yet,' said the young girl, as she skipped down the street holding her father's hand.

When they reached home they could not move in the house and everyone seemed to be talking at once. 'Go and wash yer hands, Ellen, they're mucky,' Mary shouted to her daughter.

Everyone sat down for their tea: home-made jam, potted meat and dripping sandwiches, with currant and iced buns to follow, and finally jelly or trifle. When they had all finished eating, Mary put the birthday cake in the middle of the table, and John lit the candles. Joe stood on his chair and after three goes he managed to blow the flames out. They all sang happy birthday and Joe helped his mother to cut the cake.

Fun and games followed as they all played hide and seek, pass the parcel, and musical chairs, while John played the mouth organ. All the children stood up and said a nursery rhyme or sang a song; then it was time for everyone to go home.

That evening Joe and Mary sat talking together. 'Well! It seems ter 'ave gone off very well,' said Joe, and inclined his head to the fire. 'Everyone seemed ter 'ave enjoyed it.'

'Yes, yes,' replied Mary. 'At least we didn't 'ave any watterworks. To say they were all only babbies they were quite good.'

'I don't know about 'em being babbies. Some of 'em could eat as much as an 'osse!' John laughed as he spoke.

'Oh, I like to see 'em eat at that age, it means that they're 'ealthy and growin'. I know when I was their age the food wasn't there ter eat,' said Mary, rubbing her legs. 'Me pins are killin' me! Ah've been on 'em all day.'

'Yer can 'ave a lay in termorrow, there's nowt ter get up for,' replied John.

'Except the sound of four little feet about 'alf past seven in the mornin',' said Mary, pulling a face. She went into the kitchen.

John sat pondering; he thought that they had been lucky the way that things had turned out. The house was nice and comfortable. They had bought a new green horsehair couch in the front room that went well with the large sideboard they had brought from Doncaster, and they still had the two blue painted vases, with the matching quartz clock belonging to his parents, that stood proudly on the mantel piece. Hanging on the wall were two large frames containing butterflies shaped to form a heart, which John and his father had caught in Doncaster wood. The floor was carpeted and there was a home-made clippy mat in front of the hearth.

In the kitchen they had lino on the floor, and the wooden table and chairs from their previous home. Looking into the heart of the fire John could see the large black kettle puffing away. He lifted the chenille cloth from the floor, took the kettle from the fire and poured the boiling water into the brown teapot; he added two spoonfuls of tea, stirred it round, put the lid on the teapot and covered the pot with a hand-knitted cosy.

'This is what yer need, Mary, a nice strong cuppa,' he said to his wife.

Mary placed a large brown earthenware bowl, which she called a panshion, containing flour and lard on the hearth at the side of the fire. When it had warmed for about an hour, she took the bowl into the kitchen, kneaded the contents together with other ingredients, put the panshion back on the hearth and covered it with a wet tea towel.

'What yer bakin'?' asked John.

'Some teacakes. I thought they might make a change for the babbies, and yer could take a couple fer yer snap,' replied Mary from her chair at the side of the fire.

'Did yer throw the currants in from the top er Crag 'Ill?' asked John. 'I can't even see um.'

'Shut yer gob,' said Mary laughing. 'I'll 'ave yer know that 'ave put a pound of currants in that panshion.'

'All I can say is yer must have counted um. I'll get me spyglass and see if I can see one.'

John lifted his pipe from the pipe-stand and relaxed back into his chair.

'Do yer want some tea, John?' asked Mary.

'I think I'll 'ave er slice er toast wi' some drippin' on,' said John standing up.

He went into the kitchen and cut himself two large slices of home-made bread. He went back into the living room, took the three-pronged brass toasting fork from the side of the fire grate, stuck the fork into the bread and placed it in the middle of the fire.

'Do yer want some, Mary?' he asked.

'No thanks. I 'ad some bread en jam when I was kneading the teacakes.'

'Secret eatin' eh? There's no wonder yer gettin' fat,' laughed Joe.

An hour later John said, 'I'll make the fire up, then it's up the wooden 'ill, I think; it's been a long day.'

'Yes,' said Mary, 'the babbies will be up before we get ter bed.'

Two incidents occurred the following Saturday. About nine thirty in the morning, there was a knock on the front door. Ellen opened the door to find a man dressed all in black.

'Good morning, Miss,' said the young man, smiling. 'Is yer father or mother at home?'

The young girl looked at the man with a gaping mouth and shouted, 'Dad, there's a man in black clothes at the door.'

John walked to the door and held the handle. In front of him stood a tall slim youth with blond hair and a light moustache carrying a black cap. 'Good mornin', my name is Father Macfaith. I am from the Catholic Teacher Training College at Spinkhill,' said the priest. 'The parish at Doncaster wrote and told us that yer were now residing in the village, and I have come to see yerselves and other Catholic families.'

'Come in, Father,' said John cheerfully. He opened the door wide to allow his guest to enter, and motioned him into the kitchen. 'Take a seat at the side er the fire, it's a bit chilly out. Can I make yer a cuppa tea, Father?'

'That's very kind of yerself, Mr Saul, I would love one thank you,' replied the priest with a simple smile as he sat on the chair in front of a roaring fire. 'Yer've got a nice house 'ere, Mr Saul.'

'Call me John, Father,' came the reply has he put the black kettle in the middle of the fire. 'Yes, we've been very lucky. We were a bit concerned when we left Doncaster, but it's worked out very well fer us. Mary, the wife, likes the 'ouse and neighbourhood, and the kids 'ave found new friends very quickly. I'll just fetch the tea and milk, Father.' John went quickly into the kitchen.

John came into the room and the kettle started to boil. He mashed the tea in a black ceramic teapot, saying, 'This pot was me Mam's. We only use it on special occasions. Do yer like yer tea weak er strong, Father?'

Father Macfaith stretched his right leg. 'Fairly strong, John; milk, but no sugar. I am sweet enough, me Ma always used ter say,' he said easily.

John filled a white pint pot with tea, added the milk, stirred it round and gave it to his guest. 'Yer sound a bit Irish, Father, is that correct?'

The priest leant his head back and gave out a large laugh. 'Yer've got me in one, John,' he replied. 'Fer me sins I come from County Cork, and I am proud of it.'

'You'll be able to 'ave a good natter wi' Mary, me wife. She comes from Ireland. 'Er family were tinkers; she'll tell yer all about the 'omeland.'

'Yes, I am sure she will, John, and we'll have a chat later. But the reason I've come terday is ter discuss celebrating the Holy Mass in the village. Have yer thought anythin' about it?' asked the priest.

'Yes, we've talked to the landlady of the Portland Hotel – yer passed it when yer came inter the village,' John said, and pointed to the end of the road. 'Her name is Mrs 'Annah Palmer. She says that she'll rent us a big room at the
back, on Sunday mornin's.'

'I'll go and look at the room. If it is suitable then I'll leave a note with the landlady fer you and the other families who wish to attend,' replied the priest, and stood up to go as Mary came in the back door.

'This is Father Macfaith, Mary,' John said, and inclined his head to the young man. ''E's come about sayin' mass in the village.'

Mary held out her hand. 'Good mornin', Father,' she greeted him. 'We were wonderin' about that the other day. 'As John told you about The Portland Hotel?'

'Yes,' said the priest. 'I was just on me way ter take a look, ter see if it was suitable. I understand yer also from Ireland, Mary. We must have a chat about the homeland the next time I visit.'

'I would enjoy that very much, Father,' said Mary, and smiled.

Ellen had been sat quietly on a chair at the table fascinated by their visitor in black. She had a mental image of the priest floating through the clouds on a magic carpet surrounded by angels.

''Ave yer come from 'eaven, Father?' asked the young girl. She put her elbows on the table and rested her head on her hands.

The priest gave a loud laugh. 'No, Ellen, I'm only a messenger of God,' he replied. 'I teach the word of Jesus ter help you ter be good; and prepare yer soul for ter go ter heaven.'

'My friend next door, Vicky, 'er dog died last week and 'er Dad said that 'e had gone ter 'eaven.' Ellen rocked her head in her hands as she spoke.

'I am quite sure he has,' the priest said softly, as he patted the girl's head. He turned to John and Mary, 'If all goes well we'll see you all next Sunday at The Portland Hotel. God bless you all.'

Father Macfaith made the sign of the cross and left the room.

'Well! That's a surprise, Mary,' said John, returning to the kitchen after letting their visitor out.

'Yes, and I've another one,' said Mary as she put her black leather shopping bag on the kitchen table. 'I've been ter the jumble sale at the Methodist Hall on the bottom road. Look what I've managed ter pick up.' Mary held up two white shirts with blue stripes on them. 'They only cost a penny each, and will be ideal fer work.' She took two red woollen jumpers out of the bag, and went on. 'One will fit Joe and the other Ellen. They'll look smart dressed up in the same colour.' Finally she took out some small pink and white baby clothes.

John looked at the small garments with a shock. 'They're a waste er money, we've no one ter fit them!'

'There will be next year when the new baby comes,' said Mary, and smiled at her husband.

John sat down with shock, and then his face brightened.

'No wonder yer said yer had another surprise,' he said. He stood up and kissed his wife on the forehead.

In May 1903, Walter Owen was born. Two years later in July 1905, William was the third son and fourth child in the Saul family to come into the world.

Part Two

The Prosperous Years

Chapter Three

First Aid: Small and Large

The years up to 1920 were prosperous for the majority of the miners in the country. Nottinghamshire had its own local union which had been formed in 1893, The Notts Miners' Association. The local associations where affiliated to the National Union; and were recognised by all the colliery owners. Between 1888 and 1914 there was very little change in the cost of rent, fuel and food; however for the same period wages for skilled labour increased by eighty-four per cent. There was a large improvement in the miners' wage, which explained why the colliery owners had very little difficulty recruiting labour. Between 1888 and 1920 the output of coal in Britain's mines increased by thirty-five per cent.

In 1906 John was asked to assist in the formation of a division of the St John Ambulance Brigade in Creswell. He was pleased to help because he had been a member of the Doncaster Brigade before coming to the village.

The St John ambulance was developed from the Order of St John, which was founded by Italian Catholic monks around the year AD 1000. The aim of the original members was to offer medical care and assistance to pilgrims who were travelling to Jerusalem. The order spread into many countries of Europe. The medieval monks developed the order in England, which flourished until the reign of

Henry VIII. During the king's reign, the Catholic monasteries were closed and the Protestant religion was established. This meant the loss of the order in Britain for nearly four hundred years. The St John Ambulance Association was founded in the Britain in 1877, and the Brigade around 1887.

The colliery company had their own horse-drawn ambulance which ran on wheels with India rubber tyres. The vehicle would accommodate two patients and an attendant. Their was a first aid room on the pit top, first aid posts in the mine, and the doctor in the village was easily contacted in cases of emergency.

First aid equipment would include splints, elastic band tourniquets, tins of carbolic cotton wool, and tins of boric lint with adhesive plaster, various types of bandage, sal volatile, bicarbonate of soda, olive oil, spirit of ether compound, tins of boric acid, and tincture of eucalyptus. Tools included forceps, knives, needles, safety pins, carbolised Chinese twist, silkworm gut, black and white sewing thread, kidney-shaped basins, graduated measures, carbolic soap and nail brushes.

The object in forming the Brigade was to teach its members first aid. It might be that many of the Brigade members were the first persons on the scene when an accident occurred. Their lessons included: giving help or assistance to anyone suffering from injury, such as a broken arm or a burn, either at work, or in the home. The group also learnt how to help or comfort someone who, for example, had fainted, or had a fit, until a doctor arrived.

The lessons were to be held in the Drill Hall, a large building that had been built the previous year by the colliery company for social and domestic interests of the local community. The Drill Hall was composed of a large central room with a stage, plus a small room at the rear and a small choir room upstairs.

First aid was very important in the mines. Every official working in the pit had to have a first aid certificate, and they had to take a re-examination every year. Many of the other men also took part in the St John's lessons. There was an added bonus in that people who joined the Brigade were allowed a free one-week holiday, which the unit spent at the colliery company campsite at Rhyl.

All the men were provided with a uniform and a first aid book. The classes involved every aspect in first aid including fractures, dislocations, sprains, strains, bandaging, haemorrhages, the circulatory system and organs, bruising, burns, scalding, bites, stings, artificial respiration, fits, poisoning, methods of carrying patients and many other subjects.

The meetings were usually held on a Sunday morning. There was normally an hour of lectures and an hour of practical work on a variety of subjects. The men learnt about observation for signs of injuries; how to be tactful when investigating the symptoms or history of a case, and resourcefulness in cases of emergency by using what items may be at hand. For example, they were shown how a walking stick could be used for a splint or a handkerchief for a bandage. They were taught how to instruct the patient, and any people passing by who may have stopped to help after an accident. If there were several injuries it was important to know which one required priority treatment.

A skeleton was provided by the mine owners. She was believed to have been a twenty-year-old nurse, but she was small for her age. The men called her Nelly. John brought her into the main hall where the group of men were sitting on wooden chairs. 'We 'ave a new bonniefied member,' he said to them smiling.

'She looks a bit thin!' shouted Vic Jones, one of the deputies. 'She could do with some meat on 'er bones.'

'You remember the story of Adam in the bible, when God took one of 'is ribs when 'e was asleep and formed Eve? Well, I think Nelly was formed from you, Vic. She looks a lot like you!' John said, laughing.

'There's one thing fer sure she wouldn't take much carrying on a stretcher.' Vic bent backwards and scratched his head as he spoke.

'Yer could take 'er 'ome and put 'er in a pan to make some soup,' shouted Alan Fox, a fitter in the mine.

'Yer'd need a rabbit ter chase the bones round the pan and a stone er tatties to give it some taste,' remarked John, pointing at the varnished ribs.

The class had to identify all the bones in a human body. It was a tedious job and was learnt over a period of several weeks, The normal process was to start at the head and work down.

After about half an hour the class got restless and to make a change John went on to another subject.

'Okay we've had enough of that fer today,' he told them. 'We'll ask some questions ter see if yer've been reading yer books. Vic, what would yer do wi' a man who had broken his femur in the mine and was in shock?'

'I would deal wi' the broken leg fost,' came the reply. 'I would try ter keep the bone in as natural a position as possible usin' bandages and splints. I would put him on a stretcher and make some paddin' for the soft part of 'is leg ter avoid injury. Fer the shock I assume the man's face would be pale and 'is skin clammy. Probably 'is breathin' would be irregular and 'is pulse weak. I would lay the patient down. If the stretcher wasn't available, I would put summert underneath him; cover 'im up ter keep 'im warm, and if I 'ad a warm drink I'd gi'e 'im a cuppa sweet tea.' Vic stood up and gave a small bow.

'That's good,' John said approvingly. 'Does anyone want ter add anythin' ter that?' The room went quiet and no one answered. After a few seconds John went on, 'We'll move the chairs and do some bandagin' for an 'our and then we can go hom'. There's some triangular bandages on the chair in the corner.'

When John got home Ellen came running into the house and shouted, 'Dad, Vicky next door 'as been stung by a wasp!'

'Tell 'er ter come in an' let's 'ave a look at 'er,' said John, and smiled at his daughter.

Ellen went rushing out of the back door, only to re-enter in a few seconds with her distressed friend holding her arm by the elbow.

'I tried ter swipe the wasp we me hand and it stung me,' said the small girl with a pained face, displaying a large red blob on her left forearm.

John took hold of Vicky's arm and asked his wife, 'Can yer 'eat me a needle on the fire, Mary?'

Mary found a needle in her sewing box; picked up the chenille cloth from the hearth, put it on her hand and stuck the needle into the middle of the fire. After half a minute she took the red-hot needle from the flames, held it in the cloth until it cooled, then passed it to her husband.

Vicky turned her head away, screwed up her eyes, and gave a small jerk of her arm. John punctured the red blob on the girl's arm and squeezed the spot until the sting came out. He applied a small amount of dilute ammonia to the wound, dried it off, covered the infected area with bicarbonated soda, and finally wrapped a clean bandage around the bare arm.

'There you are, young lady!' he told her. 'Make sure that yer keep the bandage on for a couple er days.' He squeezed the small girl's hand and let it go.

'Thanks, Mr Saul,' said Vicky. She smiled at him and skipped out of the house. However, even John's knowledge and skills of first aid were to be of little use for what was to happen in the Saul family a few months later.

★

In the summer of 1907 Joe came home from school feeling sick. Mary took a look at her son, and felt his head which was very hot.

'Go ter bed, son,' she told him, 'and I'll bring up a 'ot watter bottle.'

Joe went up the stairs without a hint of a complaint. Mary went into the kitchen, boiled the kettle and poured the hot water into a brown stone bottle. She wrapped a tea towel around the bottle and took it up to Joe's bedroom. Mary laid the bottle between the white sheets at the bottom of the bed. 'Be careful yer don't bon yer foot on the bottle,' Mary reminded her son. Joe nodded but did not seem to care.

When John came home from work, Mary asked her husband to go into the village and ask Dr Wood if he would call and see their son after he had finish evening surgery.

John went into the village to find the red and white barber's pole that hung outside the doctor's home – red signifying blood and white bandages. He entered the treatment room, but only the doctor's wife was at home.

She was a small chubby woman, with brown hair, blue eyes and a round face. She was wearing a nurse's uniform.

'Would yer please ask the Doctor ter call at number 45 Duchess Street and see me son, Joe Saul?' asked John, his head bent.

'He's out on a call, Mr Saul, but I will pass the message on when he comes home,' Mrs Wood replied, smiling into John's sad face.

'Thank you, Mrs Wood. I think that kids are more trouble then all the ponies I 'ave ter see ter in the mine,' replied the ostler as he turned and walked out of the surgery to make his way home.

About seven o'clock there was a knock on the door. Mary answered the knock and opened the door to find Dr Wood standing on the pavement. He was about twenty-five years old, six foot tall, and slim, weighing about eleven stone. He had dark curly hair, brown eyes and a downward curling dark moustache. He was wearing a black trilby, dark suit, white shirt, thin black tie and a dark horsehair overcoat.

'I am very sorry ter call yer out, Doctor,' Mary said, bending her head, 'but Joe came home from school running a temperature and looked very sick.'

'Good evening, Mary. It's okay, I had another call on Duke Street anyway so it is not a problem.' The doctor took off his cap and passed it to Mary as he entered the door.

Ellen poked her head around the kitchen door. ''Ello, Doctor, have yer come ter see our Joe?' she asked. ''E's ever so poorly; 'e don't even went ter talk ter me!'

The doctor bent down and looked into the young girl's face. 'Hello, Ellen,' he said. 'I hope you've been looking after him until I arrived.'

'I wanted ter give 'im me bread and jam, Doctor, but 'e wouldn't take it! 'E told me ter go away. Are yer goin' ter make 'im better, Doctor?'

'I hope so, Ellen. Now look after your two little brothers won't you,' replied the young man. He stood up, brushed the child's cheek and turned to her mother.

"E's upstairs, Doctor,' she told him. 'I put 'im straight ter bed. 'E must be sick because 'e' 'asn't 'ad 'is tea.' Mary tried to laugh.

The Doctor followed Mary up the stairs, and into Joe's bedroom. 'Hello, son, how are you feeling?' he asked cheerfully.

"Ello Doctor,' replied the young boy very weakly. 'I feel red hot, I've got pains in me tummy and me 'ead aches.'

'Well let's have a look at you, then.'

The Doctor pulled back the bedcovers to examine the limp body, and could see that Joe was sweating heavily. He took out his stethoscope to listen to the boy's chest and placed a thermometer in his mouth. After a full examination he put the covers back over Joe's fevered body.

'He's got fluid on his chest and is running a temperature of a hundred and four. I would keep him warm and give him as much hot liquid as he can drink,' said the doctor as he put his instruments back into his black leather bag. 'I'll leave a bottle of laudanum. Give him two teaspoonfuls, three times a day; it will help to make him sleep. Make sure that his urine bottle and bedpan are well cleaned and disinfected when he has used them. As far as possible I would keep the other children from directly touching him – although I know that will be difficult if not impossible.'

The doctor left the room and Mary followed him downstairs. 'What d'yer think 'e's got, Doctor?' she asked anxiously.

'We have one or two cases of typhoid in the village and it looks possible that is what Joe has contracted,' Dr Wood replied.

''Ow do yer feel that 'e caught it?' said Mary, inclining her pained face.

'The disease is passed from one person to another,' the doctor told her, 'mainly through water or food. When someone has the condition it is excreted from their body by their faeces and urine, for example. When they go to the toilet and do not wash their hands, and then handle food, water, or pots and pans, they may pass the fever on to other people. The problem with typhoid is that humans who do not show symptoms of the fever can also pass the illness on to other people. They are called carriers, and are a big problem. The trouble is that they probably do not know themselves that they are able pass the fever on to their families and friends. Carriers can be a major problem to a community, especially when they work in food shops.'

Poking out of the kitchen door were the three small faces of Ellen, Joe and William. The doctor bent his knees to look into the children's faces. He said gently, 'Your brother is very, very sick, and I want you all to be good and help your Mam and Dad as much as possible. Will you do that for me?'

'Yes, Doctor,' came the three serious voices in unison. The Doctor stood up, patted the three heads, and took three sherbet lemons out of his pocket. He gave one to each child.

'Thank yer, Doctor,' came back in unison as the children smiled and thanked their visitor.

Mary opened the door, and the Doctor walked into the street. 'I'll pop in tomorrow, Mary, and remember what I said about washing the bed pan and urine bottle,' he told her.

'Yes, Doctor, and thank yer fer comin',' answered Mary. She closed the door and stood with her back to it for support, with her shoulders bent low, carrying a worried and concerned mind.

John had been to Nash's shop on the Main Street – or bottom road – to buy a pint of methylated spirits for the stove. He entered the back door a few seconds after the Doctor had left by the front. The children turned to their father. 'Dad, Dr Wood gave us a sherbet,' said Ellen, smiling.

'Did yer thank 'im fer the sweet?' asked John, as he took of his flat cap and hung it on the door.

'Yes, Dad!' The children all spoke together.

Mary came into the kitchen looking very solemn. 'Trouble?' John asked, looking sadly at his wife.

'The doctor thinks Joe's got typhoid.'

Mary plopped her body into the chair at the side of the fire, put her head into her hands and started to cry.

John gave a small whistle of despair. He walked over to his wife and put his arm around her shoulder, allowing her to cry. When she lifted her head John looked at her and tried to smile. 'There's a few men at the pit wi' the same trouble,' he said gently. 'They say it can be serious, but don't worry, Joe's young an' strong. If anybody can pull through it, 'e can. I bet 'e'll be runnin' about like a madman in a couple er days or so.'

'We've got ter make sure 'is bedpans and water bottles are washed in disinfectant when 'e's used em. And the kids mustn't touch them, and if possible not Joe either. That'll be easier said then done.'

As Mary spoke, she lifted her sad face to look at her husband. 'We'll 'ave ter change the beds round. Bill and Walt can sleep in the small bedroom and Ellen will sleep wi' us fer the time bein'.'

John nodded his head and said, 'We'll 'ave ter leave our door and Joe's door open. If 'e gets ter bad, one of us might 'ave ter stop up wi' 'im all night.'

The doctor visited every day for the first week. The house seemed to be in chaos. Mary kept Ellen away from school as a precaution for herself, and her classmates, knowing that she could inadvertently pass the fever on to the other children. She was of great assistance to her mother in looking after her younger brothers, helping to make the family meals and clean the house, and allowing Mary to give as much attention as possible to her oldest son.

Joe had a high fever and consumed only liquids. Mary was so concerned that she sent for Father Macfaith who give the boy the Sacrament of Last Rites; and the priest promised to say a mass every day for the sick child. Mary laid her mother's black rosary beads on Joe's pillow. They were over a hundred years old, and her family believed that they had great healing powers. John put the large black family bible on a table at the side of the child's bed, with two candles continuously burning on either side of the sacred book. John and Mary stayed awake on alternate nights to care for their son and keep him as comfortable as possible.

Then the fever reached a peak. At times Joe did not even know who was in the room. He was excreting a greenish soupy diarrhoea; on occasions he was delirious. Mary and John were constantly emptying and washing bedpans and laundering clothes. Joe's parents continuously washed his face with a cold damp cloth to cool him down. During the third week he developed coloured spots on his chest and abdomen. By the fourth week the patient was gradually improving and a calm peace began to settle on the Saul household.

'He seems to be on the mend now, Mary,' said Dr Wood as he stood at the end of the bed smiling at Joe. 'You have been lucky that no one else in the family has contracted the fever.'

'Yes, Doctor, in a sense it's a miracle,' Mary replied. 'But only me an' John 'andled the bedpan and we were careful with it, especially when the kids were about; and we put Joe's waste in a separate toilet ter what anyone else used.'

The doctor turned and looked at Mary and said, 'You were sensible, but you still had a lot of luck, especially with the two boys. They are still little more then babbies. It could have been much more difficult for them if they had caught the fever. There have been six deaths in the village with the same disease. Thankfully it seems that the worst is over for Joe now. The serious cases develop ulcers in their intestine, and fluid spills into the abdomen and then the peritoneum goes septic. On other occasions the patients bleed to death internally.

'It's also been a bad time for the business people. Two of the grocery shops have had to close in the village because they had to throw all of their stock out, and have no money to replace the wasted food.'

'Yes, Doctor, it's been a bad time for the village all round. We've a lot ter be thankful ter God for. Both you and Father Macfaith have been a tower er strength to us,' Mary said as she walked to the top of the bed and tidied Joe's pillows. She pointed to her son. 'Do yer think 'e can get up for a short time, Doctor?'

'Only for a hour or so until he feels stronger, but I don't think it will be too long before he is runnin' around the house like his old self.'

As they walked down the stairs, Mary said, 'At least we can all get some sleep. I think we could do with it.' After being handed his cap, the doctor went through the front door and stood on the pavement. 'Thank you again for your kindness and help, Doctor, I don't know what we would have done without you.'

'Oh that's all right, Mary,' he replied. 'If they had all turned out the same way Joe has I would have been very thankful. He was a strong, healthy, and well-fed lad before he became sick and that gave him lots of resistance when he needed it most. Goodbye, Mary, and look after yourself; it as been a difficult time for you. I don't want to have to come to see to you next time.'

'Goodbye, Doctor, and God bless,' said Mary, 'and thanks once again.'

The Doctor put on his cap and walked down the street. Mary closed the door, said a small prayer of thanksgiving, went into the kitchen, filled up the kettle and put it on the fire.

Chapter Four

Village Entertainment

In 1880 there were five businesses, excluding farmers, in Creswell. In 1904 the number had risen to around twenty-five. By 1908 there were over sixty-five tradesmen; and the count was increasing annually. Shop owners in the village included: ten grocery and confectionery shops, nine butchers, six fish dealers and four boot repairers. Many of the butchers had their own slaughterhouses and the fish came directly from Grimsby on special fish trains. One shop that opened at 17 Welbeck Street, owned by William Ellward, was a great novelty to the villagers because it sold a new invention called a talking machine.

In 1859, Leon Scott produced from a human voice, the first recorded sound, using a cylinder, a funnel and a pig's hair. The energy produced from the sound of a human voice made the hair vibrate from side to side on a piece of smoked paper, which had been attached to the cylinder.

It was Thomas Edison in America who reproduced the first sound of a human voice in the following way. He attached a mouthpiece to a brass cylinder, into which he cut some small circular grooves on the cylinder's surface. He covered the inside of the cylinder with tinfoil. The cylinder was then made to rotate using a spindle, or axle. A needle was placed on a vibrating disc, sometimes called a diaphragm, inside the cylinder. The needle was then placed against the foil that was covering the cylinder. When someone spoke into the machine, the energy produced from the sound of the voice caused the diaphragm and needle to vibrate against the tinfoil inside the cylinder. The vibration of the needle made dents in the tin foil as the cylinder, with the circular grooves, moved round on its spindle.

Then to play the sound back, another needle was attached to the diaphragm and placed against the cylinder wall containing the original tinfoil with the dents on the surface; these had been produced by the needle from the original sound of the human voice, as the cylinder rotated on the needle. These vibrations reproduced the sounds that were roughly the same as the original voice.

Alexander Graham Bell, who produced the first telephone, also invented a talking machine called a graphophone. The sound that he reproduced was cut into a wax surface inside a cylinder made from cardboard. The two inventors, Thomas Edison and Alexander Bell, exchanged ideas to reach the final product.

Emile Berliner, an American scientist living in Washington, produced a more successful five-inch disc, and a machine giving a reasonable recorded sound. He subsequently produced a master disc, which enabled large numbers of copies to be reproduced from the original single record. He called his machine a *gramophone*. The Gramophone Company was formed in England around 1898.

On the death of his brother, the artist Francis Barraud acquired a dog named Nipper and a gramophone. One evening the dog was listening intently to a voice on the gramophone, which he associated with his old master. Barraud decided to paint the dog paying great attention to the gramophone. The record company, RCA (The Record Company of America), was impressed with the painting and adopted the picture of Nipper; and the artist's title for the painting, *His Master's Voice*, as their trademark; which for many years was probably the most famous trademark in the world.

*

Ellen came rushing home from school one evening during the autumn of 1908. Her white socks had slipped down to her ankles, and the belt was hung loose on her blue and white striped dress. Mary was stood by the oven with a cloth in her hands, her face flushed by the heat from the fire, waiting to take out a large oval earthenware dish containing a lamb casserole. John was sat in a wicker chair at the side of the fire chewing a small piece of twist; at his side was a black round spittoon containing sawdust.

'Slow down girl you'll break yer bleedin' neck before yer get in the door,' said Ellen's father dryly.

Ellen ignored her father's verbal chastisement and turned to her mother, saying, 'Mam, what do yer think they've got at school?'

Mary looked at her daughter and sighed, she was pregnant again and her temper was short. 'Good God, Ellen yer look like a bag er rags! Pull yer socks up and put yer belt back on yer dress,' she snapped.

Ellen was undaunted by her parents' reception. She followed out her mother's instructions and continued in a gleeful voice, her eyes shining, 'They've got a gramophone and some records!'

Mary turned round to see the glow on her daughter's face, which gave her a special feeling of personal happiness;

although pride refused to allow her to show it. Instead she asked, ''Ow did they come by that? They were collecting pennies only last week fer new books and pencils!'

'Mr Bainbridge from the pit and the Duke of Portland paid fer it,' said Ellen. 'The Duchess presented it to Miss Doris Vardy – her father 'as the printers on Duke Street – this afternoon. Oh Mam, the Duchess looked smashin'! She 'ad a gold necklace on, a bright yellow silk dress and black high 'eels; yer should 'ave seen 'er!' Ellen's feelings and emotions could be heard in her voice.

'I am surprised that thcy've kcpt that er quiet,' said John, leaning forward in his chair. 'Usually there's talk in the pit when Bainbridge turns up, and the whole village normally knows fer weeks on end before the Duchess is comin' inter Creswell.'

'I think one of the teachers helped the Duchess with the embroidering of some curtains at Welbeck Hall, and it was given as a goodwill gesture,' replied Ellen as she hopped from side to side an one leg. 'Miss Vardy reckons it will go well in the classes with the piano.'

Mary lifted the casserole dish out of the oven and placed it on the hearth. She took off the lid, stuck a fork into the meat and smelt the aroma. The fork came out of the meat with ease. 'Well that's done, anyway,' she remarked, mainly to herself as she replaced the lid on the dish.

Joe came into the house and through the back door carrying Ellen's coat. 'Yer'd forget yer head if it were loose.' Joe looked angrily at his sister, with animosity in his voice, as he threw the coat on a chair.

'Why don't yer go ter 'ell and back?' his sister retorted, with venom in her speech. 'I wanted ter tell Mam about the gramophone and I forgot it.'

John lifted his head. 'All right, you two,' he said, 'I'll get yer a pair er boxin' gloves.'

Mary looked at her daughter and pointed to the coat. 'Go and 'ang the coat up. I don't want the place lookin' like a pigsty!'

Ellen obeyed her mother's instructions. When she returned to the kitchen, Joe turned to his mother and said, 'You'll never guess who she's been dancin' with? It was Bill Snape who lives in the Model. 'E's always chasin' after 'er.'

'Oh *Joe!*' cried Ellen indignantly as she went red in the face and clenched her fist. 'Ye're nothing but a shit-stirrer.'

Mary looked at her husband. His head was bent low and he was chewing his tobacco, called thin twist, very quickly, trying to stop the smile coming on to his face, that was caused by the remark made from his ten-year-old daughter.

Turning back to her daughter, Mary said, trying to sound angry, 'That's enough er that language, young lady, or I'll 'ave ter wash yer mouth out with soap. You'll 'ave ter confess that sin ter Father Macfaith when yer go ter confession, and say some penance.'

Ellen looked pleadingly at her, mother and tried to control her temper. 'Well 'e *is,* Mam! It was Miss who paired us all together, and what about 'im? 'E was dancin' wi' Rose Turner of Welbeck Road.'

'I only danced once wi' 'er, but you 'ad at least five dances we 'im,' retorted Joe with a smug grin on his face. He sat down on a chair at the side of the table.

'All right you two, break it up. Go and wash yer 'ands, and get yer brothers from the backyard, or the tea'll be cold before yer sit down ter eat it,' said Mary, lifting her head and pointing to the back door.

Five minutes later they were all sitting around the wooden table for their tea. As usual John said grace before the meal: 'Bless us, O Lord, and these they gifts, which we are about to receive from they bounty, through Christ our Lord,' – and they all replied in unison, 'Amen.'

Lamb was John's favourite meal. He enjoyed the special taste of the meat, and its greasy gravy, which added taste to the potatoes, onions, carrots and swede that went to make up the tasty dish.

'The meat tastes good, Mary,' he told his wife.

'I got it from Knowles in the village. I roasted it first ter get some of the fat out, and ter make some drippin' for yer snap,' replied Mary, as she stuck her fork into a piece of potato and placed it into her mouth.

Ellen wanted to talk about the gramophone. 'Yer should 'ear all them smashin' records, Mam! There's all kind of bands and people singin' which makes some lovely dancin'. I think their goin' ter take it ter the Drill Hall when they 'ave dances,' she said excitedly.

'What kind of dances 'ave they got?' Mary asked, looking at her daughter with affection.

'All sorts.' Ellen's small eyes twinkled as she replied. 'There's some folk dancin'; we all do them, even the five-year-olds in our Walt's class. There's a mazurka – it's a Polish dance, like a polka. Some of the girls have clogs and do clog dancing. There's a cha-cha, rumba and a smashin' waltz. I think Miss said a man called Strauss wrote it.' Ellen glowed with her new-found knowledge.

John looked up from his plate. He had a lamb bone in his hand which he had been sucking clean of meat.

His daughter continued, 'There's some band music and Miss says that we can learn ter play some instruments. She says she's goin' ter talk ter the band leader at the pit.'

For afters there was rice pudding with a spoonful of home-made jam stirred into milk dish to give an added taste, followed by a strong cup of tea.

Mary looked around the table at her family to see if they had all finished eating their food and said, 'Okay, Ellen, you wash the pots and Joe will dry. Bill and Walt can clear the table and take the cloth off.' Just like a well oiled machine everything was completed efficiently and quickly. Anyone walking into the house would never have known that just a few minutes earlier that the Saul family had been eating their evening meal.

Ellen was still full of the day's events. 'Are you goin' ter play the mouth organ, Dad, and we can do some singin'?'

'I would ask yer Mam about that,' said John. 'Maybe she'll sing a coupler old Irish ballads.'

'Come on, Mam, let's 'ave a sing-song!' Mary was encouraged by the four children's voices.

'All right but only a couple, cos I'm feelin' just a bit tired and it's gettin' late.' Mary sang *Galway Bay* and *When Irish Eyes Are Smiling* accompanied by John on the mouth organ. Then all of the children each sang a song; joined by much laughter and clapping, until Ellen looked at her mother who was bent forward in her chair with cramp.

'Dad, look at Mam, she's poorly!' cried the girl in despair.

John turned and looked at his wife. 'Joe,' he said urgently, 'go inter the village and fetch the midwife, yer know where she lives. Ellen put the kettle and a pan full of water on the fire, and get some clean sheets outer the bottom drawer, in the chest of drawers in the lad's bedroom.'

The children quickly obeyed their father's instructions. John slowly and carefully helped his wife up the stairs and into bed. He stayed by her side holding her hand. Eventually the midwife came up the stairs breathing deeply to catch her breath after rushing down the street. 'How is she, Mr Saul?' she asked, anxiously.

''Er pains are rapid. I don't think she'll be ter long,' John replied, and stood up. 'I'll go and see ter the kids. Give me a shout when yer want anythin'. The kettle's boilin' and there's clean sheets on the dresser.' He turned, left the room and went down the stairs, thinking, here we go again.

The children all looked nervously at their father. 'All right, you lot,' he said quickly. 'Get yerselves ready for bed, and be as quiet as yer can. Yer Mam won't want a lot er noise tonight.' They all trundled up the stairs. But Ellen turned and looked at her father. John walked over to his daughter and rubbed her hair. 'Go on!' he said. 'It'll all be all right. It'll be over in a bit.'

Ellen climbed upstairs, but went into her mother's bedroom, sat on a chair at the side of the bed, and took her hand. Mary smiled at her daughter.

'One day it will be yer turn,' she said softly. 'It's always better when it's over. Go ter bed now.'

Ellen left the room but could not sleep. She went downstairs to sit with John.

John and Ellen drank about four cups of tea and walked up and down the kitchen floor waiting nervously. About four hours after the midwife had arrived, on 2nd September, 1908, Charles Saul came into the world with a loud cry and a small slap on the bottom from the midwife. Ellen and John ran up the stairs.

'You've got a new brother,' said Mary smiling at her daughter.

''E looks like er skinned rabbit wi' air on,' replied Ellen.

'You were like that; and look at the rattle we get from yer now!' said John, and put his arm round his daughter's shoulder. 'I think yer Mam could do wi' a cuppa and some peace and quiet for a bit – come on.' They both went downstairs feeling content, and greatly relieved that everything had gone well; and mother and baby were both in good health.

★

Another landmark in the history of the village was the opening of the first picture house, The Electric Palace, in 1910, which was built by Rodgers the builders.

A film is a series of hundreds of still photos that are observed one after the other at a very fast speed in quick succession. Cameras at the end of the nineteenth century could take sixteen pictures a second on rolled celluloid film.

A British photographer Eadweard Muybridge was the first person to succeed in taking photographs of an animal in motion when he worked in California in the USA. He produced a series of photos of a running horse, by arranging a row of cameras set in a sequence across a field with strings attached to the camera shutters. When the horse galloped across the field, it ran through the strings; they snapped and set off the camera shutters in quick succession, producing a series of pictures of the animal galloping.

In 1893, Thomas Edison produced the first moving picture machine, using a black and white film that ran for about one and a half minutes. William Frise-Greene from England invented a moving camera in 1889. It was George Eastman in America who invented the first roller film.

The Lumière brothers held one of the first public screenings of a projected moving picture in Paris on 28th December, 1895. The first public performance in England was around Whitsuntide in 1896.

The first picture house in Creswell was built on King's Street. Every weekend, the owners showed a special film matinee for the children. One rainy Saturday morning Mary decided that Joe, Walt and Bill could take Charley to the matinee for a treat, hoping that he would sit quietly through the films. The four lads walked from their home down Duke Street and across Elmton Road to the cinema.

The public walked up about four concrete steps to the main entrance of the picture house. This consisted of two large red doors leading to the foyer. To the left of the entrance was a sweet kiosk. To the right was the ticket office. There was a balcony upstairs and the prices of the seats were 3d and 2d, and a ground floor – known as the chicken run – where the tickets were 1½d and 1d. The Sauls waited patiently in the queue of children for their tickets. Charley did the honours. 'Four one-pennies, please,' the boy said, and reached out his hand to pass the coins to the lady behind the counter.

'You're a bit small. I can hardly see yer nose,' she said, and smiled at the child as she handed him the tickets.

Charley smiled back. 'I've come ter see some cowboys and Injuns,' he told her.

The boys turned to the left and there was a man with a red cap and a black uniform stood just outside the inner cinema door.

'This way, Charley,' Joe said and pointed his finger to the man. 'Give the Mister the tickets.'

The child handed the tickets to the man. He punched a hole in them and gave the tickets back to Charley. 'I've come ter see some cowboys and Injuns,' said the child, smiling.

'You'll see two lots today young man,' said the man, returning the smile. 'Your seats are in row twenty, halfway down.' He opened the door to let the children into the main theatre.

The walls of the room were painted with white lead-based paint. The floor was made of concrete covered with lino. There was about forty rows of red leather-backed seats; the front seats were the cheapest and those at the rear the most expensive. Each row was sloping slightly to the front of the cinema. There was an aisle an each side of the room leading from the back of the hall to the front. At the front of the theatre stood a man with a film projector. The projector was pointed directly at a large white screen. To the left of the screen was a black upright piano and a stool.

The four lads sat in their designated seats and waited for the theatre to fill. A large woman weighing about eighteen stone, with short-cut white hair and a black dress, entered the room and sat on the piano stool. The lights were turned down, and the projectionist started to show the films. The lady played the piano in response to the speed of the film. The young audience were enthralled by the six films that were shown. Each film lasted around eleven minutes and included comedy, drama, cowboys and local newsreels.

When the matinee was over and the lights turned on, Joe looked at his youngest brother. His shoulders were hunched, his hands clasped between his knees, and he was perspiring with sweat from the excitement.

'Did yer enjoy that?' Joe asked. Charley nodded his head, seeming unable to speak. 'Come on then, let's go 'ome and yer can tell Mam and Dad what yer've seen.'

When the boys got home John was peeling potatoes in an iron bowl on the kitchen table, Mary was cleaning the brass ornaments and Ellen was raking the fire ready to throw on a bucketful of coal.

Charley sat on a chair at the side of his father. Ellen turned to look at her youngest brother as she straightened her back and rubbed the coal dust from her hands. She remarked in a very jovial fashion to her youngest brother, 'Well! 'Ave yer been ter the flicks?'

The young lad rubbed his bottom on the chair and nodded his head. 'There was some cowboys and Injuns,' he said.

Joe was standing with his elbow leant on the mantelpiece over the fire grate. He turned to look at Ellen, and said, 'They showed six films, two cowboys: one was a train robbery, the other was fightin' the Indians – I think Charley liked that one. One of the actors was William Hart.'

John gave Charley a piece of raw potato that he had just peeled. The child placed it in his mouth and munched it. 'What other films was there on, son? enquired his father.

Charley swung his legs on the chair and lifted his head. 'There was a funny man with a black hat, moustache and baggy trousers.'

'That was another right Charley,' said Walter, trying to get into the family conversation. 'It was Charlie Chaplin. They always 'ave at least one of 'is films on.'

Joe turned again to Ellen. 'There was one of your favourites as well,' he said, 'with Douglas Fairbanks an' Mary Pickford in a drama.'

'Oh!' cried Ellen. 'I think Douglas Fairbanks is smashin'. I could watch 'is films all day.'

John turned back to Charley who seemed to be continually turning his head round the room to look at the rest of the family. 'Was the show good then, son?' he asked.

Charley nodded his head and out came a big surprise. 'There was this whackin' great woman playin' the piano,' he ventured.

Mary looked at John who raised his eyebrows and then lowered his head. 'That is a norty thing ter say, Charley,' rebuked his mother. Charley bowed his head. 'The lady is fat because she's sick.'

'And she's ever so nice,' butted in Ellen. 'She sometimes plays the piano fer us at school.'

'Okay!' said John, 'break it up now; let's get the dinner ready. There's a football match at the pit, and me and Joe are goin' ter watch. Ellen wants ter go ter the choral society at the Institute; she can walk up wi' us.'

After the children had gone to bed that night Mary heard a noise coming from Charley's bedroom. She went quietly upstairs. Her son was fast asleep, but she could hear him say, 'Bang, bang. I've killed another Injun.'

She went silently downstairs and into the kitchen and looked at John. 'I think 'e's killin' Injuns,' said Mary, smiling.

John bent forward in his chair with his pipe in his mouth and said, 'I think yer could say that all was quiet on the Western Front.'

Chapter Five

Snow White, the Big Porky

By 1912 many changes had occurred on the national front. In the 1906 general election, the Liberals were swept into power with a large majority of a hundred and thirty seats. The Prime Minister was Sir Henry Campbell-Bannerman; and for the first time in parliamentary history there were thirty Labour MPs. The election balloting system had been introduced in England in 1872.

The new Chancellor was David Lloyd George who assisted in bringing in various revolutionary laws, including the first Old Age Pension Act on 1st January, 1909. The act provided people over seventy, who qualified under the legislation, an income of five shillings a week. 1909 also saw the introduction of the first Labour Exchange Act, and 1911 the first National Insurance Act, whereby the workers paid a contribution towards the benefits that they received.

The first Morris Oxford was built in 1911; the first petrol driven car had been invented by Gottlieb Daimler in 1887. The first Labour newspaper, the *Daily Herald* was printed on Wednesday, 25th January 1911.

On the local scene Emerson Bainbridge became chairman of the Bolsover Colliery Company on the death of Sir Henry Hall in 1909. When Bainbridge died in 1911, he was replaced as chairman by John Houfton.

In 1910 the colliery company employed a slack bobby to cover all of their mines. His job was to ensure that the miners used only forks – not shovels – in the pits to ensure that, as far as possible, only lumps of coal were removed from the mine.

The Saul family had another increase, when their second daughter Margaret was born on 11th December 1911. Ellen had left school at the age of thirteen and was working in service at a large house belonging to a family who owned a hosiery mill in Mansfield. She was only allowed to visit home every other Sunday. John's youngest brother Joseph had come to work at Creswell; he was to be the assistant ostler in the mine. Joseph and his wife Emma were living on Fox Lane in Whitwell, about two miles from the colliery.

John's prime aim in life was to ensure that his family were well clothed and fed. He had rented an allotment at the side of the Crags for several years. Along with the gardening, he also kept some chickens to provide eggs for the family, but he felt that some of the land could be put to better use. It was only by chance that the opportunity to carry out his wish came to pass.

Early in 1912 John was visiting Sam Jones, one of his workmates who lived with his father on Ernest Hopkinson's farm at Bonbusk. John was standing in the farmyard waiting for his friend to appear. To pass the time away he was looking over a fence into a pen containing an excessively obese white sow who had given birth to a large litter of piglets.

The sow was laid on her side and fourteen hungry mouths were sucking at the teats on her belly. John noticed at the side of one of the hind legs of the mother was a very small piglet who was left on its own, seemingly unable to get to its mother for sustenance. The farmer was walking across the yard and came up to talk to the ostler. John pointed his finger at the lone piglet.

'It looks like that little 'un can't get ter feed, Mr Hopkinson,' he said.

'That's the runt of the litter,' replied the farmer. 'There's usually one or two. They normally end up dyin', they're normally pushed out by the others as they get stronger, and the little 'un gets weaker.'

'What do yer want fer it?' asked John on the spur of the moment.

'Yer can have it for nowt,' replied the farmer. 'I'd be pleased ter get it out the road. I'd probably end up buryin' it anyway. But you'll 'ave ter bottle feed it for about twelve weeks.'

John took the piglet home in a cardboard box, and collected some sawdust from the colliery joiners, which he used for bedding the animal down. The children were delighted to take turns to feed their new pet. They called him Snow White, because of the colour of his skin. When the pig was twelve weeks old, John took the animal to live in a shed at the bottom of the allotment.

The pig was fed on vegetable toppings, thistles, dandelion leaves, garden weeds, potato peelings, swill and the family waste. This was occasionally topped up by cereals that John was able to buy from the farm. It was now October and there was an 'r' in the month; it was accepted that pigs were not killed until there was a letter 'r' in the month, the summer months being too warm for the meat. John decided that the animal was getting too big – it was over twenty stone in weight – and he asked Mr Hallam the butcher on the corner of Duke Street if he could slaughter the pig. Arrangements were made to take the pig into the slaughterhouse one Monday afternoon, after the butcher had killed and dressed the animals that he was to sell in his shop the following week.

John went to his allotment early the morning that Snow White was to be killed. He had arranged for a horse and cart from the farm to collect the pig and deliver it to the butchers. Walt and Joe were going to help their father with the work, but neither of then wanted to do the job, feeling with sadness that Snow White was still a family pet. They remembered when he was small enough to carry in the palms of their two hands.

John opened the shed door where the pig had been living for most of his life. The pig turned round to look at its master, probably wondering what he was doing in the shed so early in the morning.

'I'm sorry but it's yer last day on earth terday, yer've been a good 'un and I'm sure God ull look after yer soul,' John said, stroking the pig's head.

Picking up the fork, John started to clean out the manure from the shed door to make it easier to walk the animal out when the cart arrived. He had filled his barrow full of the waste and was about to take it to the bottom of the garden when Joe and Walt came through the gate at the bottom of the allotment. Joe walked halfway down the path when he picked up an object that was half buried in the soil and looked at it carefully.

When the boys reached their father he did not look or sound very pleased, refusing to admit that he was a little sad about the day's proceedings.

'About time you two got 'ere. I thought yer were stoppin' in bed all day,' he mumbled.

'We had ter help Mam ter get some coal in fer the fire, and I didn't want ter see Snow White killed anyway,' retorted Walter.

'Well yer ain't got much choice, I can't say that I am all that excited meself, but it's got ter be done. What's more yer won't be worryin' too much about Snow White when yer eatin' yer dinner. Or do yer intend starvin' fer a month?'

Joe noticed the tension in the air between his father and brother, and decided to change the subject. He handed the object that he had just picked up in the garden and held it out to his father.

'What do yer think that is, Dad? It looks like stone but it's flat and it's got some marks an the edges, look,' he asked.

John took to object from Joe and laid it on the palm of his hand. 'That's a piece er flint that the Stone Age men used fer tools when they lived in them caves over there, some ten thousand years ago,' John replied, pointing to the limestone rocks across the road that overshadowed the allotment.

The boys turned and looked at the rocks with a different eye, and then turned back to their father. 'What did they do wi' em?' asked Joe. 'They only look like slices of white cobbles.'

'That's what they are really,' replied John. 'The flints are smallish white cobbles; they may 'ave been small sea creatures millions er years ago and they fossilised inter stone. The Stone Age men used ter chip the slices off the flints usin' other stones, and turned 'em inter tools fer killin' and skinnin' animals. When yer go inter Mr 'Allam's slaughterhouse, if yer look close, you'll see that many of the butcher's tools resemble the flint tools that they used thousands er years ago.'

'What type of animals was there at that time?' asked Joe, seeming to become more interested.

'Small 'uns, I think,' said John, as he tilted his flat cap and scratched is head. 'Animals like 'ares, rabbits and small mammals. They sometimes made arrows ter shot at their prey; or just knocked the animals down with their tools. Then they 'ad different shapes of tools fer flayin' the skins. Anyway, that's enough 'istory fer today. Come on let's get on and get this shed cleaned out, or Snow White won't be goin' anywhere. It's like a swamp in there.'

The lads helped their father clean out the shed, whilst Snow White watched in shock and horror at the proceedings, wondering what all the fuss was about.

John dug some potatoes out of the ground and picked a large cauliflower for dinner. He was putting the vegetables into his wheelbarrow when the farmer arrived with the horse and trailer to collect the pig and deliver it to the slaughterhouse.

John tied a rope loosely round the animal's neck and walked it slowly into the trailer. The pig began to snort and grunt – probably sensing danger for the first time – but he was very tame; and he was allowed to walk at his own pace.

They reached the slaughterhouse. Mr Hallam, a tall thin young man, with light coloured hair and a cherry shaped face, wearing a white overcoat and thick black knee-high leather boots, came out and looked at the pig.

'He's a big 'un, John! We'll 'ave ter pole-axe him, that's the easiest way fer an animal that size. You've certainly fed him and looked after him well!' he said.

The men walked the pig into the slaughter hall and fastened him to an iron chain in the corner of the room.

The slaughterhouse was clean and tidy. The ceiling and walls were painted white, and the floor was made of concrete. There were two large hemp ropes in the middle of the room, which pulled the dead carcasses for dressing from and to the floor, when the animals were being flayed during dressing and cleaning. They were hanging from two large wooden beams in the ceiling.

'Go and get them buckets in the corner, Joe,' ordered John, pointing to where four containers were stacked in a pile. 'You'll be able ter catch the blood and use it fer makin' black puddin'.'

'Okay, everybody ready?' asked Mr Hallam as he looked round the room. Taking the pole-axe from the hook on the wall, he efficiently stunned the animal in one quick blow. He speedily slit the animal's throat as it lay on the floor. Joe collected the blood as the pig's reflex movements pumped the fluid from its body. He then stirred the fluid quickly round in the bucket, to remove the solid particles that would make the liquid set. Joe then put the full buckets containing the red fluid against the wall to cool down.

Walter looked a little pale. John turned round and put his arm around his son's shoulder. 'The worst is over now. Mr 'Allam was quick and Snow White didn't feel any pain,' he said reassuringly.

Walt nodded his head, not feeling too confident that his father's words were correct, and still remembering the times when Snow White was just a small piglet.

When all the blood had drained from the pig's carcass, the butcher brought out a large iron bath. He placed the body in the bath, covered it with very hot steaming water; and commenced to scrape all the hair off the pig's skin. When the task was completed the animal's body was taken from the bath and hung in the air to remove the internal organs. Finally the carcass was split down the middle.

The butcher picked up the pig's bladder and gave it to Joe. 'I think yer can use that fer a football, can't yer?' he asked.

Joe took the organ, smiled and replied, 'Gee thanks, Mr 'Allam, we 'aven't 'ad one of these fer ages.'

Although Walter was upset by the events, he was still fascinated by the butcher's work. He turned to his father and asked, 'Do we look like that inside, Dad?'

'You'll 'ave ter ask Mr 'Allam about that,' said John, pointing his finger to the butcher.

'We're very similar,' replied the butcher, who had been listening to the conversation. 'We have the same type of digestive system and a layer of fat round our bodies. But a pig's fat is white; ours is slightly yellow.'

'There you are,' said John looking at his son, 'knowledge fer nowt. But, I think it's illegal ter kill people.'

'Thank goodness it is! I don't think that I could do that. Although on occasions there are one or two of my customers I would like to strangle,' said Mr Hallam, laughing.

'And one er two kids on occasions as well!' said John, and pointed at Walt with a smile on his face.

When the work was completed Mr Hallam turned to John and said, 'I'll sort all the usable bits and pieces out that yer can eat for yer, and yer can collect 'em tomorrow morning. It looks like the weather's in for a cold spell, which will be useful until you've got the pork butchered.'

John turned to the butcher, 'Thanks very much, Mr 'Allam. 'Ow much do I owe yer fer the work?'

'Two bob, John, if that's okay.' Mr Hallam bent his head slightly forward as he replied.

Taking out a silver coin from his pocket, John said as he passed it to the butcher, 'I was tellin' the lads about the 'istory er the Crags and the flint this mornin', and the coin reminded me about somethin' my mate told me at work the other day. 'E does a lot of readin' and reckons that the first coins that were made were the value of animals. A cow was worth the first gold coin, and a sheep was the value of a silver coin. I don't know if he was pullin' me leg but that's what he reckons.'

'I don't know, John, but it sounds possible,' replied the butcher in a thoughtful voice. 'I do know that many of the first tradesman sold their goods fer barter.'

''E my have been pullin' me leg as I said. Anyway! I'll see yer tomorrow and thanks a lot, Mr 'Allam,' concluded John. He turned and waved his hand as he walked through the door.

'Goodbye John and thanks fer the business,' the butcher replied as the door closed.

The following morning all of the Saul family were awakened early so that breakfast could be finished before the pork was collected from the butcher's shop.

John was in the slaughterhouse before seven o'clock to collect the full buckets of blood, and the leaf fat from inside the pig's belly wall. When he arrived home, he cut up the fat in small pieces and mixed it into the liquid blood. To this mixture he added oatmeal and various spices, including salt, pepper, sage, thyme and onions. After stirring the mixture together, John then filled it into the cleaned skin of the pig's intestines. He then went to the pantry and took out a large round iron cooking pan, the one that Mary used for making home-made jam. The black pudding was placed in the pan, which was then half-filled with water. The pan was placed on the fire and allowed to cook for about thirty minutes.

'You'll be able ter 'ave yer favourite breakfast for a couple er weeks,' said Mary, as she made sure that the pan was safe on the fire.

'Yes; that's the first job done,' John said, and turned to look at Mary. 'I'll go and get the carcass next. I want the barrow out er the out'ouse.'

'Take one er the lads with yer and send 'im back wi' the liver. I've got some large onions, and together they'll make the dinner.'

Mary turned to look at the fire again to ensure it was hot enough to heat the oven and boil the pan.

Charley was stood in the yard throwing a ball at the wall when John collected the barrow. 'Come 'ere a minute son,' called John. 'Go and get a pan from yer Mam and come wi' me ter 'Allam's.'

The boy rushed into the kitchen, collected the utensil from his mother, and ran down the street after his father. Ten minutes later he was back in the house holding out a pan full of offal at arm's length to his mother.

'That was quick,' said Mary. She turned her head and smiled at her son; his face was flushed and glowing red, and he was breathing heavily.

'I ran cos I didn't want ter drop it,' explained Charley as his mother took the cooking utensil out of his hands.

'All right, go back and see if yer Dad wants any help,' she replied, 'but walk don't run, or you'll trip yerself up.' The boy turned on his toes and walked slowly through the door. Mary watched her son go and with a smile on her face she shook her head and thought, I'll give him five yards before he starts ter run.

To see the faith and spirit of her children always brought
happiness to her mind, as she considered there would be
plenty of times in their lives when it would be destroyed by
the cares and worries of the world and the people who live
in the world. But, until that time came, the beliefs and
enthusiasm that brightened their young lives should never
be discouraged.

About thirty minutes later John and Charley returned
home with a barrow full of meat. Mary had cleared the
kitchen table for John to put the produce on. She looked in
shock at the amount of meat that she could see. 'I never
thought there would be as much as this,' she exclaimed.

'That's only 'alf of it the rest is yet ter come,' said John
with brightness in his voice.

Mary took her hand from her mouth. 'I never thought
that Snow White would ever grow ter be as big as that! 'E
was so small when 'e was born.'

''E just seemed ter plonk the weight on when he went
down ter the allotment. The shed wasn't too big, but 'e was
content and that's why 'e grew. Still, 'e's made some good
meat.'

'I think we'll 'ave enough meat ter last fer six months if
we can keep it in good condition. 'Ave yer worked out how
yer goin' ter butcher it?' Mary enquired as she scratched
her head and held her back.

'I am goin' ter cure the 'ams and bellies,' John said, and
laid his hand on a large leg of pork. 'We've got plenty er
salt, sugar and saltpetre. We can 'ang em up outside in the
out'ouse at the bottom of the yard. The loin can be used fer
chops and joints; and the shoulders, we can cut inter small
cubes fer makin' up. That parts up ter you.'

'I was goin' ter make some pork pies, 'aslet and sausage
meat.'

Mary rubbed her hands at the thought of all the work involved. She went on, 'We can do some savoury ducks and I've bought some red skins from Mr 'Allam so we could cook some polony. Some of the pork cubes can be salted down and used at Christmas. There's only twelve weeks ter go and we can 'ave another treat then. There's the fat as well; we can render it down and use it fer lard, and the kids will eat the scraps when the liquid's been pressed out.'

Charley turned and looked at his mother, and asked, 'What are we goin' ter do we 'is 'ead, Mam?' The boy pointed at a large pig face staring at him from the table.

'I'll show yer what we're goin' ter do wi' that,' said Mary. She went to the cutlery drawer and took out a sharp knife. She returned to the table and scored many lines with the knife into the rind – the outer skin of the pig – all round the head; about a half inch distance apart. She rubbed salt all over the head, then she went to the pantry to get a large cooking apple. The apple was placed in the pig's mouth; the head was put on an iron tray, and was then slid into the hot oven.

Charley's face was aglow, 'What 'appens when 'e eats the apple, when it's in the oven, Mam?' he asked.

'I think 'e's gone past eatin' anythin',' Mary answered, looking down at her son and smiling. 'Come on there's a lot ter do.' She placed her hand on her son's shoulder and they walked back to the table.

It took Mary and John, with the help of the children, over three days to complete their work. On the night the pork had finally been butchered and prepared John sat in a chair by the fire, lit his pipe and began reminiscing. 'Do yer know, Mary, it's strange but we would never 'ave been doin' all this work if I 'adn't 'ave 'appened ter be visiting on the farm in January and seen that sow, and the little runt in a litter er pigs! And that meat will feed us all fer at least two months, and some of the neighbours 'ad a joint as well. Dad always used ter say that God was good and will look after 'is own.'

Mary sat at the other side of the fire watching the glow of the red, blue and yellow flames. She said quietly, 'My Mam always used ter say that yer life was planned and yer can't do much about it even if yer wanted to. Yer just 'ave ter let it take its own course. I can remember that she once read me palm when we was sat at the fire just like we are now. I would only be about five years old I can still see her face now. She told me that I would have nine children, I would have my troubles but I'd always 'ave enough ter eat. Do yer know I often think about reading the kids' palms, but I never get round to it... maybe one day I will.'

'Well from what yer mam said, that's probably where the pig comes in, but yer've only got six kids,' replied John as the puffs of grey smoke rose from his pipe. 'But I suppose that there's still time yet.'

Mary looked into the fire again to watch the glowing embers, which for some reason brought a kind of peace into her mind, little knowing that her mother's prediction would eventually come true.

Chapter Six

Mabel and the First World War

On 1st August, 1914, Kaiser Bill's Germany declared war on Russia. On 3rd August, Germany declared war on France. On 4th August, Germany invaded Belgium, and on the same day Great Britain declared war on Germany. By the end of 1914 there was an entrenched line, occupied by soldiers, stretching four hundred miles across France to Switzerland.

So began the Great War, which was to last until 11th November, 1918 when Germany surrendered. Of the young men who served in the forces for Britain between 1914 and 1918 nearly ten per cent, around three-quarters of a million, lost their lives; and millions more were injured.

Many of the miners volunteered for the armed forces. The mines were working to full capacity to provide the country's energy. Collections were organised in the colliery villages to send gifts to the fighting troops. New weapons, including U-boats, tanks and combat aeroplanes were first introduced during the Great War, or First World War, as it was later called.

Throughout the Nottinghamshire coalfield, a small levy was taken from the miners' wages to help finance an ambulance service for the wounded troops on the fighting fronts.

The unions agreed not to take industrial action during the war. They agreed with the Government that any unsettled disputes should go to arbitration. The shortage of manpower because of men joining the forces meant that women were employed in the factories and on the farms for the first time. By 1918 over three million females were working in this type of environment for the first time in British history. On a national scale, between 1914 and 1918 wages roughly doubled. However the cost of living rose by one hundred and twenty per cent for the same period, so real wages actually fell. The miners' wages and coal distribution were brought under the authority of a Government coal controller.

At the start of the war Herbert Henry Asquith was Prime Minister. He resigned in December 1916, to be replaced by David Lloyd George. In June 1917 Winston Churchill became the Minister for Munitions.

Rationing was introduced in Britain in 1917. Sugar was the first item to be rationed; other products followed when necessary.

Joe Saul had left school in 1913 and became an apprentice fitter on the pit top, and Walt started work in 1916; he had become an apprentice, working with the ponies underground, later to work on the coalface. The Sauls produced their seventh child, Fanny (or Peggy as she was known), who was born on 11th February, 1914. Emma, Joseph Saul's wife gave birth to a daughter called Mabel in August 1913. Joseph was John's brother.

During the war the Saul family life went on mainly in its usual organised way. The mine was working three shifts, covering a twenty-four-hour day, six days a week. Joseph had joined the armed forces in 1916 and was a gunner in the Royal Artillery Regiment. Emma and Mabel visited

John and Mary two or three days a week. It made her feel more secure, and helped to give her comfort when her husband was away from home, especially when Joseph was on the fighting front, in the trenches in France. There was the added advantage that the three young girls were able to play together. By the beginning of October 1918, Margaret was seven, Mabel five and Peggy four.

Every Monday was wash day in the Saul's family home. This particular Monday morning was a school holiday and Margaret was at home. Her mother was pleased, because she was again eight months pregnant, and her second daughter had become very helpful around the home; especially since Ellen had gone into service.

All the men in the family, John, Joe and Walt, had gone to work on the day shift at six o'clock in the morning. Breakfast was completed; Bill and Charley had been sent down to the allotment to dig up some potatoes and carrots, and select a cauliflower for the dinner. Monday lunch was to be hash, a tasty dish manufactured from cooked cubed beef that was left over from yesterday's large Sunday joint, and a mixture of vegetables.

Margaret had just finished helping her mother to wash and dry the pots that had accumulated from the breakfast meal. She was sat on a chair at the kitchen table. Her mind was procrastinating, and she was trying to make music with a metal spoon on the wooden surface. It had been left on the table when the crockery and cutlery and been cleared away after the first meal of the day.

'Stop makin' that rattle, and put that spoon in the knife an' fork drawer,' said Mary, slightly agitated at her daughter's musical efforts, 'and then go upstairs and get the dirty washin' out er the bedrooms, or we'll never get done terday.'

Margaret deposited the spoon into the drawer, making as much noise as she could when the cutlery slid backwards and forwards, in a deliberate attempt to annoy her mother. She went upstairs, collected the dirty clothes from the three bedrooms and threw them down the stairs. Returning to the ground floor, Margaret picked up the washing and carried it into the scullery.

Mary already had a copper full of boiling water ready to commence the work when Margaret returned with the dirty washing. She filled some of the hot liquid into a barrel-shaped corrugated metal container, called a dolly tub; she sprinkled a small amount of washing soda into the container and placed a dirty shirt into the tub to soak. She then stirred it round with a poncho, a round wooden stick that had about three wooden prongs on the bottom and looked like a stool with a long handle. A few minutes later the shirt was removed from the tub. The garment was then rung out to remove some of the liquid, and placed on a corrugated metal scrubbing board. The shirt was then scrubbed with a block of hard yellow soap. The next stage was to rinse it in cold water, to wash out the soapsuds. The shirt then went through the mangle, to remove as much of the water as possible. This was where Margaret was a great help to her mother.

The mangle consisted of a large metal frame holding two round wooden rollers in adjacent positions. Attached to the rollers was a turning handle.

'Put the shirt inter the rollers,' Mary ordered her daughter, 'and catch it at the other side.' Margaret placed the shirt in the middle of the roller and Mary turned the handle. Margaret moved round to the other side to collect the drained garment, neatly folded it, and placed it into a round wicker basket. This procedure was carried out for every item that was washed.

A pumice stone was used to scrub badly soiled clothes; polly blue bags were used for whites and starch for stiffening collars.

It was raining, and Mary knew she could not hang the washing on a line outside to dry. She told her daughter, 'Go and get the clothes 'orse out of the out'ouse; put it in front er the fire. Put the clothes on it as we do 'em. The underwear can 'ang on the fireguard. At least we can get some of 'em dry. And wipe the clothes 'orse down before yer put the clothes on, it'll be dusty.'

Margaret followed her mother's instructions and placed the wooden frame in front of the fire and hung the shirt on it. They carried this process on for most of the morning, only stopping occasionally for a cup of tea. Sometimes they had the help of Peggy, who was more of a hindrance than a help; but her mother encouraged all of her children to help with the household chores, as she believed that not only was it good training for their later lives, but it helped to keep their minds occupied and make them more independent.

By twelve o'clock most of the clothes had been washed. Mary placed two flat irons on a stand in front of the fire to heat up. They were to be used for pressing the clothes.

Mary went back into the scullery to continue the wash day when Emma and Mabel entered the back door. 'Yer just in time,' Mary said to her sister-in-law, 'can yer keep an eye on the irons fer me, the're in front er the fire? The fireguard's up, but I don't want the lasses ter go touchin' em.'

'Yeah, I'll see ter that,' said Emma as she took off her coat. 'I've just done our washin'. I am pleased there's only two of us, I wouldn't want ter wash fer your lot!'

'A large family 'as advantages at times.'

Mary stood up and stretched her back. 'But,' she continued, 'there's no doubt at all, when it's wash day it's a big disadvantage especially when it's rainin'! Still I don't think I would want it any other way.'

Emma took off her daughter's coat and hung it on one of the hooks behind the door. Mabel went to play with Peggy, who had grown tired of the washing and was reading a book on the kitchen table.

Bill and Walt returned from the allotment with the vegetables for lunch and placed them on the table. 'Do yer want me ter peel the taters for dinner,' Emma called out to Mary.

'No, the two lads can do that,' came back Mary's reply, 'It'll keep 'em outer mischief and they're doing nowt else.'

'Oh, Mam!' came two voices in unison. 'We've only just come in! Can't we 'ave er minute?'

'No, yer can't,' said Mary. She stood in the doorway. 'You'll only end up messin' about, and the way I feel at the moment, if I get too much noise you'll end up wi' a clout. So get on wi' it.'

'No rest fer the wicked,' Emma said, and smiled at her two glum-faced nephews.

Walt went to get a metal bowl from under the sink and filled it with cold water and Bill took two knives out of the cutlery drawer. They both sat down in front of the table at the side of Peggy and Mabel and started to peel the vegetables. Peggy turned to her brothers and asked, 'Can we help, Walt?'

'No yer can't,' shouted Mary from the scullery, 'ye'll both end up gettin' yer dress sleeves wet, and there'll be watter all over the floor. It's damp enough terday wi'out you two chuckin' watter about.'

The two girls looked at the door sadly. Peggy turned to her cousin and said in a quiet voice; 'I think she's got out er the wrong side er the bed this mornin'.' The two girls giggled together as the held their hands over their mouths.

'I'll pretend I didn't hear that,' said Mary. She stood in the doorway and poked a finger at her four-year-old daughter.

Emma changed the subject, observing that tempers were getting a bit frayed. 'Do yer want me ter do some ironin', Mary? I think the irons are 'ot enough now ter press the clothes.'

'Yes, yer can do. The ironing board's 'ere,' replied her sister-in-law.

'I'll get it, it's a bit 'eavy, Aunt Emma,' called Bill as he walked into the scullery.

Bill deposited the thin cross-legged wooden table in front of the fire at the side of the clothes horse. 'There you are, Aunt Emma,' he said with a smile.

'Thank yer, Bill,' said Emma. She moved the fireguard round and took one of the hot irons from its stand in front of the glowing fire, and started to press one of the men's shirts. White steam rose from the damp garment. She called out, 'There's a bit er damp in the clothes, Mary. It's goin' ter be a foggy day in London town in 'ere before these are all done.'

Mary came to the doorway; she stood up straight holding her back.

'There's nowt yer can do about it. It's just one er them days.' Mary looked at her sister-in-law with a pained expression, turned her head and went back into the scullery.

By three o'clock all the washing and ironing had been finished and dinner was ready for the three hungry men coming home from work.

John was the first to arrive home. He put his snap tin under the kitchen sink and went into the back room where everyone seemed to have gathered. 'It looks like paddies bar in 'ere. Why is everyone in the one room?' he said.

'It's rainin', Dad and we can't go out.' Charley stated the obvious. 'Anyway it's nearly dinner time and ah'm starvin'.'

'Yer always starvin'. If yer put some weight on it wouldn't be ser bad ye're like a streak er pump watter,' said his father.

John turned and looked at his wife, who was sprinkling gravy salt into the hash with one hand and stirring the home-made concoction with a spoon in the other hand. For something to say, he asked, 'Dinner ready?'

Mary turned her head to look at her husband. 'It won't be long. Ye're early, John,' she remarked.

'Only about five minutes; I came up the pit a bit earlier then normal, and there was nowt ter do so I called it a day,' replied John. He took off his coat, hung it up behind the door, and changed the subject of the conversation. ''Ow's terday gone?'

'The weather's not helped, but Emma and the kids 'ave been a good 'elp and we've got finished washin' early.'

Mary turned her head back to look at the hash, and continued to stir the food round the large brown earthenware pot.

John turned to look at Emma. ''Ave yer 'eard anythin' from Joseph?'

'Not a thing,' said Emma, and twisted the cuff on her dress sleeve. 'I write ter 'im every other day, but it's two weeks since I had a letter back. Mind you I think 'is letters are censored, some of 'em look like they've been refastened down. I get nowt for a month, then I get a load all on the same day.'

John went and stood with his back to the fire and spoke slowly. 'There's a man who's just come back ter the pit after bein' in the trenches in France. They've kicked 'im out er the army because 'e's lost an arm. 'E was tellin' me that it's like a livin' death. It puts yer whole life inter perspective. 'E says that yer lay in them trenches waitin' fer an order ter charge, and wonder if it's goin' ter be yer turn next. And when nothin' 'appens yer think well 'ave got another five minutes ter go yet. 'E says yer don't think about petty things like coal, clothes and food. Ye're just livin' from one minute ter the next.'

John stopped talking when he heard the jocular voices of his two oldest sons, and turned to see their arrival through the back door, ''Ere comes trouble, Mam,' called out the ostler.

'Eh, Pop,' shouted Joe. 'We've got a large crowd in 'ere terday! There's more people in 'ere then watches the colliery football team on a Saturday. It's not difficult ter see it's rainin'. I don't now what's er matter we yer, at bit er watter never did anyone any 'arm.'

'It won't do you two any 'arm 'ither; go and get a wash in the outhouse and put some clean things on, don't bring them dirty clothes in 'ere,' Mary shouted at her sons.

'Keep yer 'air on. We're on our way, Mam. Dinner smells good, anyway,' said Walt. He waved his arm at his mother as he left the room.

'It'll be dished up when yer get back. There's some jam roly-poly and custard fer puddin',' Mary called after her sons.

Dinner was over in about half an hour accompanied by the usual non-stop chattering. John stood up from his chair where he was sitting at the table and went to put his overcoat on. 'I'm gain' ter the allotment, Mary, ter see if the 'ens 'ave laid any eggs. Maybe Emma would like ter take a few 'ome when she goes,' he suggested.

'Can me and Mabel come, Dad?' Peggy implored her father.

'Yer'd better ask yer Mam and Aunt Emma; she might not want Mabel ter come – it's still rainin' – and they've got ter walk home yet,' John replied.

The two girls looked at their mothers expectantly. 'All right, yer can go,' said Emma, 'but make sure yer've got yer 'at scarf and coat on; and don't go playin' in the puddles; you'll get yer shoes and socks wet through.'

The girls rushed for their outdoor clothing and quickly followed John through the back door. On reaching the footpath they walked down the street side by side, John holding a hand of each girl, one at either side of him, as they skipped and pulled at his arms.

'We've got another pig, 'aven't we, Dad?' Peggy asked her father quizzically, hoping to have a look at the animal.

'Yes, but 'e's only about four months old and ye're not gain' ter look at 'im ter day, because it's wet and you'll only get messed up; there'll be trouble, and then yer mam ull 'ave me guts fer garters, if yer go back dirty.'

The three ramblers arrived at the allotment and walked in single file down the path to the hen shed. John opened the door and the hens started to cluck. Peggy turned to

Mabel and said, 'They're singin' they always do that when yer open the door.'

'It sounds like me Dad when 'e's in the bath on a Friday night when 'e's at home,' put in Mabel as she leant her head to the side of the shed to listen to the birds.

'I'm not quite sure whether yer Dad would take that as a compliment or an insult,' John said, and raised his bushy eyebrows at his young niece.

They were lucky; twelve eggs had been laid. Peggy picked up one of the eggs and gave it to her niece. 'Feel at that Mabel; it's warm and the shells all smooth and smashin'!' she said.

Mabel took the egg and put it near her cheek. 'They've been cookin' 'em,' said the young girl with surprise in her voice.

'No,' said John, 'the eggs come outer the chicken's belly and it's warm when it drops on the floor. Then the chicken sits on it ter keep it warm. It's a natural thing fer em ter do.'

'Why don't we sit on eggs ter keep 'em warm, Uncle John?' asked Mabel. She bent her head to one side in a quizzical mode as she looked at her uncle.

John lifted his flat cap and scratched his forehead, which was his usual reaction when lost for words. 'It's a long story,' he replied slowly, 'but 'ens sit on their eggs to keep 'em warm until a baby chick 'atches out er the shell. But we use the eggs ter eat. One day yer mum ull explain all that ter yer.' John put the eggs into a wicker basket and turned to the girls. 'Come on then, let's go 'ome; we've got what we came for.'

The three explorers returned home. Mabel was full of the story of the hens, which she relayed to her mother in a slightly exaggerated fashion. John went into the kitchen drawer; took out a paper bag, and placed six eggs into the bag. He then gave the bag of eggs to his sister-in-law. 'That ull make a change fer yer breakfast, fer the next couple er days,' he said kindly.

Emma took the bag, smiled, and said, 'Thanks, John. I can make Mabel an egg custard as well. It's 'er favourite puddin'.' Emma looked at her daughter. 'Well! It's time we went 'ome young lady. Thank yer aunty and uncle fer a nice day.'

Mabel went and kissed Mary and John on the cheek, and they were ready to go home. 'See yer in the week, Mary,' Emma called out to her sister-in-law as they went through the back door. They both waved and were gone.

Mary expected to see her two relatives either on the following Wednesday or Thursday, but they never turned up. When nothing was heard by Saturday morning Mary began to worry. John had been working in the morning but was home by twelve o'clock. He was hoping to watch the colliery teams football match in the afternoon. Mary had his dinner ready but she spoke to him about her concern for Emma's absence through the week.

'I'll take er walk up ter Whitwell before I go ter the match and see if anythin' is wrong,' said John as he was eating his meal.

On arriving at Fox Lane, John was shocked to find that Mabel was seriously ill. She had a fever and was suffering from convulsions. He returned home to give the news to Mary. She was very depressed at the news but could not leave home because she had only a month of her pregnancy to go.

'Either me or one er the lads ull 'ave ter visit every day and see if there's owt we can do,' said John, with worry in his voice. "I 'ope it wasn't caused when Mabel went down ter the allotment on Monday.'

'Yer can't blame yerself fer that, John.' Mary consoled her husband. 'It was rainin' when they came, and it was rainin' when they left. Mabel always walks in the rain. She's done it dozens er times when they've come 'ere and she's never even caught a cold.'

A daily vigil at Whitwell was kept up by the Saul family, but Mabel never improved. They were all savagely struck by the disaster, seven days later, when Mabel died suddenly, aged five. The death certificate said influenza and convulsions. Her mother was by her bed when her small daughter took her last breath.

The news so distressed Mary that only two days later, on 16th October, she gave birth to her fourth daughter Agnus, three weeks before she should have come into the world. Mary was ill and stopped in bed for over a month, and it took a great effort from her family to pull her through. What should have been a time of happiness at the arrival of her new baby, became one of the saddest periods of her life.

Part Three
Hard Times

Chapter Seven

After the First World War

Great celebrations followed the Armistice of 11th November, 1918. However, after a brief spurt of prosperity following the war, there began a period of unease and decline for the British people. The interest owed by the Government on the national debt had increased drastically by fourteen times its value between 1913 and 1920. The problem was made worse because there had been several large loans made to Russia during the Tsarist era, and the money was unable to be recouped, due to the Bolshevik takeover. Britain has always been a major importer of goods, and our exports before the war were vital to our balance of payments. However, many of these export markets were lost during the war. The coal industry suffered from German and Polish competition. The cotton industry lost out to Japan and India; and the merchant shipping had rivalry from the USA and Japan.

In 1913 the output in coal from Britain's mines was two hundred and eighty-seven million tons, of which eighty-four million were exported. Many of the exports were never recovered after the war. There was also a decline in the home markets. Various reasons for the loss of trade can be given and they included:

Germany had to make compensations for damage that it had caused during the war. Some of this was paid with free coal which went to former British markets.

The high price of British exported coal during the war encouraged other countries to find alternative methods of energy, for instance Switzerland, Norway and France utilised natural waterfalls.

There was an increasing substation of coal with other forms of energy. For example, many ships changed from coal to oil as an energy source.

Industries such as iron and steel were becoming more energy efficient, with improved methods and appliances, requiring less coal.

There was also great unrest in British industry. In many working sectors there were several strikes for higher wages in 1919; militant groups included the police, the cotton industry and railway workers.

On the political scene, in 1918, women over the age of thirty were allowed to vote for the first time, adding over eight million voters to the electorate (by 1928 the female voting age was reduced to twenty-one, the same age as men). The first woman MP, in 1919, was Viscountess Astor.

The Notts Miners Association, the local miners' union, were in dispute with the colliery owners. They were demanding the removal of forks and screens – a type of sieve – from all mines in the area, and their replacement by shovels. Secondly, they campaigned to remove the butty system of paying wages (the butty system meant a number of men who worked in a small team and were paid by an overseer called a butty). Thirdly, they attempted to improve the wages of haulage hands and other selected groups.

A ballot was taken for industrial action by the miners' union at the end of January 1919. The result showed a majority vote in favour of strike action. The mines in Nottinghamshire ceased working on 19th March, 1919.

The only men that the union would allow down the mines during the dispute were deputies to inspect in districts, safety workers and the horse keepers who looked after the welfare of the ponies.

*

The first morning of the strike John was out of bed by 5 a.m. as usual. Putting on his clothes, he went downstairs and fried himself some bacon and eggs for his breakfast. After slicing some bread, he made four dip sandwiches from the fat that the bacon had been cooked in, and put them in a paper bag ready to take to work for his snap. He took out a knife and fork from the cutlery drawer and sat at the table to eat his meal.

The house seemed so still. Usually one of the lads, either Joe, Walt or Bill, who had started work in July 1918, were awake and walking around the rooms at this time of the day. He felt a little concerned that he was the only one in the family who was going to work. He did not like the strike but he thought that the men should stick together. However, his early childhood had taught him to believe that the bosses had all the power, and he felt that no good would come from the dispute.

John put on his overcoat, placed his snap tin containing the dip sandwiches into the large inside pocket, and walked out of the front door into the street. The silence was disturbing; usually the voices of men could be heard, intermingled with the chirping of the birds, as they conversed on their way to work. Even the feathered vertebrates seemed to be on strike. The only sounds he could hear were produced by the hobnails of his boots when they struck the ground as he walked along the footpath leading to the mine. He heard too, the whistling of the wind as it blew past his ears, and the heavy breathing from his smoke-filled chest.

The emptiness of the street seemed to double its width. Making his way up Morven Street, he missed the smell of the smoke that normally came from the house chimneys; normally it was rising from the fires that the men would usually have lit before they went to work; they would warm their homes for their families when they got out of bed on a chilly morning.

Going over the iron bridge to enter the pit yard the ostler heard nothing but the deafening sound of silence. To his left stood two steam engines; but there was no puffing of grey smoke through their chimneys. Between six and eight rows of empty railway wagons with *Bolsover* proudly painted on their side stood waiting to be filled; the rattling and clanking sounds that they made every day as they were shunted around the pit yard could not be heard. John reached the screens where the coal was sorted and graded. There was no chatter and laughter from the men. The stillness of the moment brought a shiver in his body. A pit yard that was so familiar to John after seventeen years seemed nothing more than a morgue.

John walked to the pit shaft. The only man there was Vic Jones, a deputy who had come to check the safety of the mine. He turned and looked at the ostler as he approached.

'We might as well go down, John,' he said. 'I don't think there'll be anybody else for a while, do you?'

'No, I don't, Vic,' came John's reply. 'It all seems like a graveyard. I've never seen it like this before, and I 'ope that I won't see it again. Usually there's someone about.'

'It's strange that it's only six months ago that the war ended. Now in such a short time there's all this trouble.'

Vic stuck his hands into his trouser pockets in a gesture of concern.

'People 'ave such short memories. There's nothin' new in the problems they're strikin' for. You'd 'ave thought they could 'ave sorted the troubles out long ago without all this aggravation. It's not the men at Creswell though – I don't think most of 'em even voted – it's them in the other mines.'

'Nonetheless, I still think the bosses ull win in the end,' said John, scratching his head in his habitual way, as the two men entered the shaft.

'Perhaps it would 'ave been better if the men had voted, then the strike wouldn't 'ave 'appened. I think ye're right about the bosses,' Vic replied, and held on to a handrail as they descended into the colliery.

The two men left the shaft at the bottom of the mine and entered the pit bottom about four hundred and forty-six yards below ground level. The pit bottom was the first section of the Top-Hard coal-seam. They walked about a mile together into the mine until they arrived at the ponies' stables.

'I'll go and do the rounds, John,' said Vic. 'I'll see yer when I get back.' Vic waved is hand as he walked away, rambling still further into the mine.

'Okay, Vic! See yer on the way back, don't get talkin' ter the ghosts comin' out er the cracks in the wall,' called John, with a chuckle.

The ostler stood and looked at the row of thick wooden stables in a pensive way. Each pony had plenty of room to turn round and they all seemed content. The animals had on their leather harnesses fastened together with brass buckles, but they were untethered and could walk about the stables freely.

They were comfortable and the air was naturally warm – a mine gets hotter the lower down it goes into the centre of the earth. There was adequate ventilation provided by extractor fans from the pit top, and assisted by other forms of ventilation underground. Each stable contained a trough to hold the animal's food, and a bucketful of water.

Each pony had his (or her) own name, usually given by the lad who would have been their first master, and the name was written on the side of the stall. These very docile animals were normally treated like pets by their masters. It was John's job to inspect all the animals individually on a daily basis; he knew them all by name and talked to them as he would a small child.

He entered the first stall. 'Good mornin', 'Ector,' he said as he patted the animal's neck. 'Yer've got a rest day er two fer a bit; yer master won't be comin' ter work until we've sorted out some little problems.'

Hector nodded his head seeming to know every word that was spoken to him, probably saying to himself, 'It's that silly old man again.' The pony was about twelve years old, around twelve and a half hands in height, and a roan colour. He had worked in the mine at Creswell for over five years. John inspected the animal's face, lifted up his lips and checked his teeth and gums. He inspected the animal's eyes which were growing dim with age, their condition also made worse through the years that he had spent in the darkness of the mine. John rubbed the pony's ears, which immediately pricked up. He felt around the animal's trunk to ensure that he was not sweating, and ensured that neither the leather nor buckles on the harness were not causing any irritation or chafing.

The ostler then picked up the equine's feet individually, and examined the shoe and ball of the foot. John took hold of the harness and walked the animal round to check for any obvious bumps or abnormalities. He checked the animal's food and water, took out a book from his coat pocket which had all the ponies names in it, and put a tick at the side of Hector. John slapped the animal's rump playfully, saying, 'You'll do, old man,' and walked into the next stable.

The next pony for inspection was called Rogus. He was a young animal, about four years old. He had only been in the mine for four months. His height was about twelve hands, and he had an iron-grey coloured coat. John followed the same procedure of inspection on the animal, who stood placidly watching the ostler's actions. When John was satisfied with the animals health and condition, he slowly worked his way down a row of over one hundred ponies who were all housed in their own stables.

It was gone one o'clock when he had finished all of his examinations of the ponies; and was sitting on the floor eating his lunch when Vic Jones returned. 'It's like watching the animals feed,' said the deputy, laughing.

'Everything okay up there?' asked John, between bits of his sandwich.

'Yes, thank goodness,' replied Vic. The structures are secure and there's no sign of gases. I checked the watter pump and that seems ter be runnin' all right as well.' Vic sat at the side of his friend and brought out his lunch.

'Yes, I was wonderin' about the pump. There's not only the 'osses but the fire points ter think about,' said John as he stretched out his legs.

The mineworkers finished their lunch and ten minutes later they started the long walk out of the mine. 'It's a funny thing, but I won't be sorry ter get out er the pit terday. It's seemed a very strange shift,' said John as they reached the pit bottom.

'Yes! It's amazin' what a difference it makes ter the atmosphere of the place ter see men walkin' about,' replied Vic. The two men reached the pit top and parted company, taking their own ways home.

When John entered the house the older part of the family were waiting for his arrival. Mary was cooking the midday meal. Joe, Walt and Bill were all sitting talking around the kitchen table. The ostler took off his coat and hung it on a hook behind the kitchen door without saying a word.

'Yer look a bit fed up wi' yerself, John,' said Mary, with her left hand on the oven door.

John took off his flat cap and inclined his head, 'Well, it's all a bit depressing really. There's no one about; and at the end er the week the men ull 'ave nothing ter spend; only a bit er union pay, and that's when the problems begin,' he said gloomily.

John sat at the dinner table with the three lads. 'What 'appened, Dad?' asked Joe.

'Nothin' really,' said John in a sombre mood. 'The only person that I saw all day was Vic Jones; and the ponies of course. It does yer good ter talk ter them at times, it keeps yer sane.'

'Yer didn't 'ave any trouble then, Dad? Like any of the other men gettin' at yer fer goin' in ter work?' asked Walt with great interest.

John looked at his son, 'No!' he said. 'I don't think there'll be any trouble like that. I reckon the men will understand that the 'osses will have ter be looked after; and most of 'em don't think that it'll last that long – or are probably 'opin' that it doesn't.' The ostler changed the subject. ''As anyone been down inter the village? Is anythin' goin' off down there?'

'I went about eleven o'clock and it all seemed like a normal day, everyone just seemed ter be carrying an as normal,' said Bill trying to get into the conversation.

Mary came over to the table where the four men were sitting, and stood behind one of the chairs. She folded her arms and asked, 'What's all the trouble about anyway?'

'There's three points really, and they're all old problems,' said John looking up at his wife's face. 'The major point is that the union want the men ter stop usin' forks and screens ter put the coal inter the tubs, and they want the men ter use shovels instead.'

'Why do the owners object ter that?' asked Mary looking at the faces around the table.

'The obvious reason is that there would be more slack in the tubs when they're filled up with shovels, and not so many lumps er coal. The owners believe that usin' forks and screens leaves only quality coal; and it is a way of reducing the workers wages. Also they'd 'ave trouble gettin' shot of all the slack,' replied John.

Bill looked at his father. 'But they do sell slack, Dad,' he said. 'I've watched tons of it go out an the Lancashire–Derby line. They reckon that a lot of it goes inter the furnaces or businesses like the steel mills.'

'Yes they do sell some slack and small coal; but can yer imagine just how much more slack you'd end up with in the tubs if the men used shovels, I bet there'd be at least twice as much and they wouldn't know what ter do we it. Yer'd end up puttin' it in 'eaps on the pit top. There's a limit ter the number of companies that would take it. Don't forget it's not just Creswell but all of the pits in Nottinghamshire,' replied John, clasping his hands together as he looked at his son.

'I suppose that the men would find it easier and quicker ter fill the tubs if they used shovels,' Mary said, and once again looked around the faces of her family sat at the table.

'There's that about it,' Walt replied to his mother's query. 'But the main reason that both the union and men object ter screens and forks is that yer can get large amounts er slack piled up in 'eaps on the floor in the mine. The slack 'eaps cause what are called Gob Fires, which produce a gas called carbon monoxide. This gas is very poisonous. The safety men sometimes use a canary to test for this gas. The bird falls off its perch when it is overcome by the gas. Explosions of firedamp (another mine gas), coal dust and other mine explosions can also produce the carbon monoxide gas.'

'But!' Mary looked perplexed. 'Why does it not do the same when there's piles er slack on the earth's surface?' she asked.

Walter smiled at his mother and tried to explain the problem.

'The air on the surface of the earth is a lot different than the air four hundred yards into the centre of the earth. Much of the air in the pit is stale – it lacks oxygen – and it 'as ter be removed by large fans on the surface, which draw it out of the mine. The air enters the pit by one shaft and goes out by the other,' he told her.

'On the pit top there's more oxygen in the atmosphere. When carbon monoxide forms the two gases combine. They produce another gas called carbon dioxide which is *not* poisonous to humans when we are on the earth's surface, in the normal air – or in the fresh air that yer keep telling us that we should get plenty of in our lungs. In truth, we breathe carbon dioxide out of our body as a waste product. Part of a deputy's job every day is to check for pockets of various types of gas and make sure that the mine is safe ter work in,' he continued.

'It's worth sayin' that if there's an excessive amount of carbon dioxide in the mine it could cause death by suffocation, because there is not enough oxygen to balance the gases in the air. It all comes down ter the amount of oxygen that there is in the air. In the mine oxygen is very limited; on the surface there's lots of it about.'

'That's all double Dutch ter me,' said Mary, rubbing the elbows of her arm. 'What are the other problems then? Why are the unions against the butty system?'

'Yer'd have ter go back inter 'istory ter explain that,' said Joe, who thought it must be his turn to speak. 'In the eighteenth and nineteenth century many mine owners employed a man ter run everythin' in the mine, and 'e was called a Butty. This man 'ired and sometimes sacked the men in the pit as and when he liked. 'E set, and paid, the wages. The butties were responsible for the mine's safety, and everythin' else involved with its runnin'.

'Not only that, 'e also owned the shops in the village – sometimes called a Tommy Shop – and 'e 'ad control of everythin', includin' the rentin' of 'ouses. But most of these men were ruthless; they got very rich at the expense of the workers who were very poor. In those days they did not allow unions, and the miners 'ad no protection from the bosses.

'In the late 1800s several mines regulations came into force. The mine owners 'ad ter employ specialised engineers and safety men. This made the mines safer; but the butties lost a lot of their power, because they no longer had overall control in the pit. Today a butty 'as charge of about five or six men. 'E gets paid for every tub er coal that his group send out of the pit, and 'e pays them for the work they do.

'The unions still feel that the butty system is unfair. They say that in many cases it is slave labour, and there are still many unscrupulous butties. In the Bolsover pits like Creswell the system seems ter work okay, because we get better, and more modern equipment then in most other mines; and the company makes a good profit.

'I suppose what the union are sayin' is that the miners in many er the collieries in Nottinghamshire don't get a fair share of the money that the owners pay out ter their butties. Which brings up the third reason for the strike, in that they want a better wage for workers like the 'aulage men who are not workin' on the coalface.'

Mary scratched her head. 'I'm more confused now then I was when we started,' she complained.

'Don't worry, Mam, it'll all come out in the wash,' said Walter, and smiled at his mother.

'Do yer think the strike will last, Dad?' Bill asked his father, changing the subject.

John sat back in his chair. 'I don't think so,' he answered. 'At the moment they want all the coal they can get their 'ands on. The Nottinghamshire coalfield is one of the biggest producers in the country. So I would think the mine owners will want ter sort it out quickly. But yer never can tell.'

At that moment Margaret and Peggy came into the house. Mary had sent them to the village for some butter and flour. They had also taken Agnus for the walk in her pram. Margaret put the food on the table, and added a small blue bag to the produce requested by her mother. 'They've got some sugar in the shop, Mam. The lady behind the counter said yer might like a pound so I've brought it. She's put it in the book ter pay at the weekend,' she explained.

'Good girl,' said Mary. 'It will come in very useful. Anyway I must get some pastry ready fer the rabbit pie, or we'll not be 'avin anythin' ter eat. The veg are cooked and we can soon 'ave some dinner.'

'Talkin' about sugar,' said John, 'the union man was sayin' that there's been complaints about the distribution er some er the food around the country and they're gettin' angry about that as well.'

'Some er the food is a bit 'it-and-miss,' replied Mary. 'Sometimes there's plenty, at other times it's very limited; or even nowt.'

The strike was over on 2nd April, and the miners returned to work. The mine owners had agreed to the union's demand. Unfortunately all of the issues remained unsettled because the agreement was not formally ratified, and some of the owners refused to honour the agreement.

Unrest continued in the mining industry. A national wage settlement of three shillings a day for adult miners was accepted by the men during March 1920. A short time later the price of household coal was increased by fourteen shillings a ton, with a much smaller rise per ton for industry. This was taken by the union as an indication that the Government intended to return the mines to private ownership.

Another wage claim was made on behalf of the colliers for two shillings a day, and a reduction in the retail price of coal. This the union believed should have been in line with the increase in wages of the miners. However, many of the districts disagreed with the union's position and felt that the claim should have gone to arbitration.

The Government refused to listen to the union. Once again the miners went on strike on 16th October, 1920.

The Government made a final offer to the unions on 24th October. The offer was related to the output that the workers produced, and included an increase of two shillings a shift. There would be an additional increase in wages based on output, and the scheme would continue until an independent wages board was set up.

Many in the union disagreed with output affecting the men's wages, because statistics had shown that since the day wage system had been introduced there was a large drop in accidents. However, the strike ended on 4th November, 1920, when the men voted to accept the offer made by the Government.

This strike became known as the Datum Strike, because of its relationship to coal output.

Once again this did not solve the many problems facing miners and colliery owners, and within a few months there was more industrial upheaval.

Chapter Eight

The Miners Locked Out

The mini-boom experienced in Britain during 1919–20 lasted for about a year; it came to a sudden halt about the same time as the Datum Strike ended. The textile and leather trades that had benefited greatly from the short boom – mainly because of shortages during the war – were some of the first industries to notice a decline in their output. Many other trades began to feel a steady downturn in their businesses, meaning short time working for men and woman all over the country. This was quickly followed by one of the worst depressions ever known in the industrial history of the country.

In 1920 the Corn Production Act, which guaranteed prices to the farmers, was repealed. This greatly depressed the farming industry, and the farm worker's wage fell dramatically.

The Government's policy was to make the pound strong in relation to the dollar. The outcome was that by the winter of 1921 there was a large collapse in wholesale prices, and a subsequent decline in trade for a large majority of industries.

Before the 1914–18 war the coal industry enjoyed a long period of constant demand and expansion. By 1921 there were one and a quarter million workers employed in the mining industry. This represented ten per cent of the total workforce in Britain. As the price of coal increased so too did the miners' wages.

The Government had taken control of the mines during the war; however, after the war, a decline in trade coupled with other problems brought about a change in circumstances. By the middle of 1920 the coal industry was costing the British taxpayer at least five and a half million pounds a month. The Government decided to decontrol the mines and return them to private ownership.

The Saul family had again increased by one. In July 1920 Mary had given birth to her ninth and final child, a girl called Catherline. There was now ten people living in a three-bedroom terraced house. Joe left the pit after the Datum Strike, and had started his own business repairing bikes in Mary's front room. Ellen came back to live in Creswell. She had married Bill Snape and they lived in one of the houses in the Model Village.

Bill Snape, called William to distinguish him from Bill Saul, was one of the union representatives for Creswell colliery. He made regular visits to the Saul household with Ellen. The natural conversation during these family reunions always seemed to be the running and management of the local mine.

In late February 1921, William had attended a union meeting and Ellen was visiting her parents whilst he was away. John, Mary and Ellen were all sitting in front of the fire in the kitchen when William came in the back door.

'Where's everybody?' William asked the trio.

'Some of 'em are in the front room,' said Mary, nodding her head towards the door. 'The others are out somewhere.'

John looked at his son-in-law, ''Ow's the meetin' gone? Yer sound a bit down in the dumps,' he observed.

William collected a chair from the side of the kitchen table and joined the group sitting around the fire. 'It's not good, I'm afraid,' he told them. 'Yer know that the mines are definitely ter be decontrolled?' They all nodded their heads. 'The act of parliament becomes law on 24th March 1921, and comes inter bein' on 31st March. The major problem is that the union believe that there will be massive job losses and large cuts in some er the men's wages. All of the men ull 'ave ter sign new contracts with their employers. Our company have offered the men terms but the wages is only slightly less then what they're gettin' now. The union reckon that it's unnecessary, but the company say they'll need the money fer contingency plans.'

Ellen looked at her husband while holding her hands out to warm them on the fire. 'If the reduction isn't too big, that's not so bad is it?' she asked.

William scratched his elbow and moved his toes in his shoes. He told her, 'It's not that bad fer us in Nottinghamshire. But in places like Cumberland the reduction in wages ull be over forty-five per cent. The problem is that the pits in them areas of the country are losin' a lot er money. When the mines were under Government control the owners and miners' wages were subsidised. From 1st April they'll lose all that money, which can only mean big job losses, and reductions in wages; or both.'

Mary looked into the fire. 'It seems that the Notts men are always goin' out on strike ter defend other people's jobs and wages,' she remarked.

'That's 'ow it is I'm afraid, Mam; and that's really the idea of the union, fer the men ter stand together against the bosses. Only this time it seems that we're fighting the Government as well.'

John scratched his forehead in a characteristic way. 'Well, what 'ave the unions decided ter do?' he asked William.

'They've refused ter negotiate on the owners' terms; and are askin' fer a national wage pool.'

William looked into the fire with a look of concern on his face.

Mary turned to her son-in-law and asked, 'Do yer think that the owners and government will agree ter that?'

'No!' said William in a sad but definite tone of voice. 'I think that the Government 'ave lost so much money on the mines that they just want ter get shut of 'em; and there's no way that a private owner ull subsidise a business that's losin' money. He might us well keep 'is money in the bank. At least 'e'd gain some interest from 'is capital. The simple truth is that where a mine is losin' money it will mean either job cuts, loss in wages, or simply closin' the pit down.'

One month later the same group of four were sat around the Saul's glowing fire after another union meeting.

'Any joy ternight, William?' John asked his son-in-law rather in hope then expectation.

William shook his head. 'There's real trouble; it's just getting' worse, The negotiations 'ave broken down all together. The union 'as decided that all the men should stop work on 30th March,' he answered.

'It won't affect you though, John, will it?' said Mary, turning to face her husband, 'but I suppose Bill and Walt ull be out again.' She gave a deep sigh. 'I think it's a good job that Joe started with the bikes, at least 'e'll 'ave a bit comin' in. The trouble is it makes things so tight all round.'

William bent his head towards the fire, 'I'm afraid that it ull affect Dad as well this time, Mam. The unions 'ave decided that all er the men are out on this strike, the safety men, ostlers, pumpmen, the lot,' he said grimly.

'That's crazy!' retorted John. He rubbed his ears as if he did not believe what had just been said, and in a retorted voice he continued, 'Yer can wind the ponies up the pit; it'll take er week or so ter get em all up. But if yer take the pump men out some er the pits ull be out er action fer months – that's if they ever open again. And God in 'eaven knows what ull 'appen if the safety men don't ger down.'

William rubbed his head. 'I think yer right,' he said, 'and in some cases they are definitely choppin' off their nose ter spite their face, but the union feel that it ull bring the whole problem ter a 'ead a lot quicker ter do it this way. One thing is fer sure we'll soon find out.'

All the workers in Britain's mines were on strike on Friday, 1st April, 1921. In truth the miners were locked out by the colliery owners. The shaft wheels had stopped going round.

John was shaving with his cut-throat razor when Bill came rushing into the house by the back door and pushed a newspaper in front of his father's face. 'Look at that, Dad,' said Bill between gasps of breath.

John took the printed material from his son and read it out aloud. 'DEFENCELESS PONIES LEFT UNDERGROUND IN BRITISH MINES WITH NO FOOD OR DRINK.' He laid down his razor and read the article. 'Why the lyin' sods! All the 'osses are up the mine on the pit surface. Ours are in the field at the back er the shaft,' he explained.

'I know that, Dad,' said Bill vigorously nodding his head in agreement with his father. 'But can't yer see that it's good propaganda fer the Government and mine owners – and it gets people against us?'

'I can see that all right,' said John sadly, 'but it's not true; and they shouldn't tell lies like that. They should check their facts first.'

All of the pits in Nottinghamshire were picketed. Once again they had least to gain from the strike. Along with the pickets, there was also a massive police presence.

Neither the colliery owners or the Government seemed anxious about a speedy return to work by the miners. They refused to open any talks until the pump men and safety workers went back to work. The unions were very reluctant, but they agreed to the owner's demand on 9th April.

A day's sympathy strike was held by the railwaymen and transport workers in the middle of April; however, it had very little effect on the miners' plight. The unions met Lloyd George, the Prime Minister, at the end of May and were told bluntly, as far as the Government was concerned, that they were under no pressure from anyone to end the stoppage. A major slump in the demand for coal meant little urgency to find a solution to the dispute.

This was the third strike that the Notts miners had taken part in over a three year period, and the local union was now deeply in debt. William had once again been to a union meeting and had met his wife at her parents' home.

''Ow does the land lay?' Mary anxiously asked William as he came into the house.

William looked around the room at the glum faces, 'It just seems ter be deadlocked I don't believe that anyone is bothered whether they talk or not,' he replied gloomily.

John bent his head to one side. He had a pipe in his mouth but there was no smoke coming out, because he could not afford to buy any tobacco. 'It seems that every time we go out on strike that it's worse than the time before. All them years with no trouble; and now it never seems ter stop,' he said.

'It's bad fer the unions this time, they've run out er funds and are goin' ter 'ave ter borrow money. Not only that; from this week, they're 'andin' out food tokens instead of 'alf the strike pay,' William told them.

Mary looked at her son-in-law with shock and dismay, 'What are we goin' ter do wi' them?' she asked.

William turned to look at Mary. 'Yer 'ave ter take em ter the shops and exchange 'em fer food. The union 'ave agreed ter pay the shopkeepers the money fer the tokens plus a bonus of six per cent after the strike's over,' he said.

'What if the shopkeepers won't take 'em? They're not all wealthy, and they'll not be able ter 'ave all of their money tied up fer weeks on end. They'll 'ave ter pay their bills ter get new stock; the strike could go on fer months,' queried John in disbelief.

'That's true,' replied William. 'One thing I do know is that Marsdens on Elmton Road ull take em; and they say they're not goin' ter ask fer the extra six per cent; so it might be worth tradin' from them; if only fer a short time.'

'That's all right,' said Mary indignantly, 'but I've traded wi' 'Iggins on Sheffield Road fer years. What are they goin' ter think if I just stopped goin' in? Don't forget that nearly everyone in the village get their groceries one week, and pays fer em the next. 'Ow do I pay fer last week's groceries? Wi' fresh air?'

'I can see that it's goin' ter be a problem fer lots er people,' said William sadly. 'All we can do is see 'ow it works out. It's just a matter er crossin' yer fingers and 'opin' that it all comes out right.'

The colliers went back to work in the middle of July 1921, on the same terms that they could have obtained two months earlier. It was in truth a very humiliating defeat for the miners and their union. However the loyalty between the districts was very strained. The Notts miners had showed great apathy, and many were to drop out of the union, which was now financially destitute, in the months that followed. They had defended a noble principle which involved standing by, and subsidising, colleagues in poorer districts. However the cost to many of the Notts miners was one of personal hardship for themselves and their families. The sacrifices that had been made had in the final assessment achieved precisely nothing.

However the strained loyalties were to have very far reaching effects in the years to come.

*

During the Great War very few cycles were manufactured in Britain. Most of the factories had been diverted into the war effort. After the war the cycles once again became available for purchase. This fact coupled with the great unrest in the mining industry, were the two major reasons why Joe Saul had decided to gamble and start his own business repairing cycles. However, the strike in 1921 had affected his trade and he had times when his work was slack.

One Saturday in the middle of June, Mary had gone into the village to help the mothers' union with some kind of social work. Not only did this give her a small break from her family chores; but it allowed her to catch up with the village gossip. She had left Joe, who was short of work, to oversee his four young sisters until his mother returned home.

Margaret was now eleven, Peggy seven, Agnus nearly three and Cath was coming up to one. It was a sunny day and the two older girls were playing outside. Joe was wondering how he could pacify the two youngsters. Looking around the room he had a flash of inspiration.

In the corner of the kitchen stood a small cardboard box which had been used to carry groceries. Joe picked up the empty box and sat with the small girls in the middle of the kitchen floor. He started to cut small squares out of the side of the box with a pair of scissors. Agnus was at the age when she wanted to talk continually, whereas Cath simply pointed her fingers at the object in which she was interested, and made strange facial expressions.

'Why are yer cuttin' them squares outer the box, Joe?' Agnus asked her eldest brother with very deep interest, as she sat beside him on the floor.

'I'm makin' a doll's 'ouse. Them squares are doors and windows,' replied Joe as he continued his mutilation of the container.

Cath took great satisfaction in picking up the small squares and throwing them around the room, giggling with delight as they skied out of her hands. However she soon got tired of the flying cardboard and proceeded to empty the bottom kitchen cupboard of pots. Joe quickly stood up and picked Cath up with one arm; with the other hand he put the pots back on to the cupboard shelves and shut the cupboard door. He then sat back on the floor with Cath on his knee, still holding her waist tightly.

Joe sat looking at the ball of Cath's feet when another idea came into his mind. Putting the baby on the floor again, he ran up the stairs and collected a handful of conkers that had been lying dormant in one of his bedroom drawers. Going back into the kitchen, he selected a packet of small pins from his mother's sewing box and sat down again in the middle of the kitchen floor.

'What a yer goin' ter do we them, Joe?' asked Agnus, her small eyes shining brightly with anticipation, as Cath wriggled her bottom on her brother's knee.

'You'll see!' said Joe as he picked out a round horse chestnut, and stuck four pins into one side. 'There yer are,' he said, smiling at his young sister, 'that's a chair.' He placed it into the middle of the cardboard box; selected another three conkers with a similar shape and followed the same procedure. Next he found a very flat horse chestnut, and again stuck four pins into the solid fruit. 'There yer are! That's er table.'

Agnus nodded her head in stunned silence, believing every word that her brother had said. But Cath was getting fed up and tried to pull the box across the floor. Joe once again sat her on his knee and gave her a rag doll which had been lying on the floor.

'Go and get some wool out er Mam's sewing basket, Agnus,' Joe said, pointing in the direction of an oblong wicker box at the side of the table. The child ran to the box and brought back a small ball of red wool. Joe broke off a piece of wool from the ball and tied it around another conker. 'There yer are! That's a sofa,' he said, and held it in the air to display it to his sister's before placing the horse chestnut in the cardboard box.

'I can't sit on that!' said Agnus indignantly.

'It's not fer you silly, is it? It's fer a doll,' replied her brother. Joe stood up and collected three empty matchboxes that were laid on the mantelpiece top. He stuck the boxes together with glue. He then pushed two pins into each box, allowing the pinheads to protrude from the outside of the containers.

Joe then placed the glued matchboxes into the cardboard box. 'There yer are, that's a chest er drawers with 'andles on. Now it's complete someone can live in it,' he declared.

Agnus rushed out of the room, brought back a large soft black golliwog, and gently placed it into the middle of the box. 'There yer are, Joe,' said the young girl proudly, 'Betty can play in 'er new house.'

Joe smiled at his sister. 'All right, but Cath's gettin' restless; let's go outside and see what Margaret and Peggy are doin',' he said.

Agnus ran into the yard, swaying as if she was drunk, followed by Joe who was carrying Cath. Peggy and Margaret were playing skipping with two other girls who lived in the street. Two of the girls were turning a rope, which had a wooden handle at each end, while one of the other girls was jumping over it. Peggy was stood waiting for her turn to skip. She ran over to Joe when she saw him coming with her two sisters. Peggy wanted to play hidey-boo with Cath, but the baby stuck her face into Joe's chest and refused to have anything to do with her elder sister.

'Come on, Peggy, it's your turn!' shouted Margaret. Peggy ran back to the group of older girls and started to skip over the rope. 'Take em down ter the sandpit, Joe,' called Margaret as she turned the rope around. 'They both like ter fill the buckets wi' sand. But you'll 'ave ter watch that they don't go inter the soot at the side er the pit. Dad put it down ter kill some insects.' Joe did as Margaret had suggested, knowing that she was in truth a second mother to all of the younger girls in the house.

Joe sat Cath in the sand, but she quickly saw a small pool of water at the side of the pit and made towards the puddle. He speedily picked her up again.

'No yer don't!' he said. 'Yer Mam ull kill me.' Joe collected a brush from the outhouse, swept the water away and put the child down again. 'Trust you,' he said, pointing a finger at his youngest sister, 'just one puddle and yer 'ad ter find it!'

About ten minutes later Joe was joined by the older girls. At the side of the sandpit was marked out several chalked squares numbered one to eight. 'We're goin' ter play 'opscotch,' said Peggy, pointing to the chalked squares.

One of the girls picked up a small flat piece of slate and slid it across the ground into the square marked one. She then hopped over the square containing the slate, and continued hopping around the remaining seven squares until she returned to the first square containing the slate. The girl picked up the slate and went back to the start and finish point. The youngster then slid the slate along the floor again and it landed in the square marked 2.

The girl carried out the same process as before, only this time she jumped over the square marked 2, which contained the piece of slate; hopped around the other squares, came back to number 2 square, picked up the slate and went back to the starting point. She then slid the slate towards the square marked 3, but it did not reach the square – she was out.

All of the girls played hopscotch in turn, until one of the youngsters managed to win, by successfully sliding the slate into all eight squares.

Joe watched the girls play a variety of games including whip and top, marbles (both chalk, which were twenty for a penny, and glass marbles which were more expensive), and various types of ball games. Some of the children had either wooden or metal wheels, which they ran along the street using a wooden stick.

Mary came home at one o'clock to a large welcome from all her family. 'Everythin' okay?' she asked her eldest son.

'Touch wood,' replied Joe tapping his forehead. 'Cath's been a bit grotty at times, other than that it's all been peaceful. At least it was dry and they could play outside.'

Mary nodded her head. 'Well, I'd better get dinner ready,' she said. 'There's some cooked veg left over from yesterday's dinner. I'll fry that up – we can 'ave some bubble and squeak – it'll make er quick meal fer terday.'

'Any gossip in the village?' Joe enquired of his mother.

'The usual births, deaths and marriages,' Mary replied, shrugging her shoulders, 'but everyone seems so depressed these days. I think a good dose er salts 'd do some of em some good at times.'

Joe had his dinner with the family and went to repair a puncture for a customer who had just left the wheel. Although he had enjoyed his morning with his sisters, he was thankful that it was not every day that he had the responsibility of dealing with the children; and he wondered what his mother would have done over the years if it had not been for the help she received from Margaret, and Ellen when she was at home.

Chapter Nine

The Recovery

The general election in December 1923 saw the Conservatives gain the largest number of seats; however, they had no overall majority. It was the Labour and Liberal Parties in an alliance that formed the new government. Labour had the largest number of seats of the two ruling parties, and Ramsay MacDonald became the first Labour Prime Minister on 2nd January, 1924. The alliance did not last long. MacDonald resigned within one year of being in office, amid unproved allegations that Russia was supplying the British Labour Party with gold, following the death of Lenin in January 1921. By October, 1924, the Conservatives were back in power. The Prime Minister, for the second time in his parliamentary career, was Stanley Baldwin.

A major piece of legislation produced by the short-lived Lab-Lib alliance was the Houses for Rent Act, from which five hundred and twenty thousand new homes were built by 1935.

The deep depression in the early Twenties was followed by a small patchy recovery in the mining industry in 1923–24. This was almost entirely due to the French army's occupation of the Ruhr in Germany. Some of the coal markets that the German mines were supplying, were taken over by the British exporters. There also a small improvement in the coal trade in home market.

Throughout the whole of the mining industry there were still large numbers of unemployed colliers. The miners' union was splitting into two distinct factions; a large group was making a pronounced swing to the left, with a much smaller minority moving to the right. One of the Notts union representatives, George Alfred Spencer MP, who was one of the group moving to the right, was destined to have a large effect on both the Nottinghamshire miners and the entire miners' union within the next two to three years.

The miners' butties had formed their own organisation based in Mansfield. Their meetings were held in many sympathetic colliery villages, including Creswell.

The development of the wireless after the war brought another mode of information to the British people. Up to this time the only information available on national and international news came from various newspapers. In 1922, King George V gave the first royal Christmas message to his people on the radio.

In 1923, The Bolsover Colliery Company bought a new social headquarters – Edwinstow Hall – on the edge of Sherwood Forest. The building was used on occasions by the miners from the colliery villages in the group, consisting of: Bolsover, Creswell, Mansfield and Rufford, later to be joined by Clipstone and Thoresby. Also in 1923, the company issued another twenty thousand ordinary shares at five shillings a share, probably to finance the Clipstone and Thoresby collieries.

The recovery of 1923–24 coincided with the building of the China Town housing estate at the top of Elmton Road in Creswell, including: Railway Avenue, Central Avenue and Wood Avenue.

Edwinstow Hall was utilised for many purposes by the company, including conferences. It contained dormitories for the guests, a gymnasium, cinema, and a concert room. Other facilities included games on the outside lawns, tennis courts, badminton courts, billiards and table tennis rooms.

Parties of employees with their wives and families, from each of the company's mines were selected to visit the Hall and participate in various competitions between the company's mining villages. The colliery bands, St John Brigades, and Boys' and Girls' Brigades all spent weekends in the retreat enjoying the company's promotions.

★

In the spring of 1924 Creswell Colliery was invited to enter two teams of four men into a First Aid competition between all of the company's mines. John, Walter, Bill and Vic Jones made up one of Creswell's teams. They had been notified of the competition for over six months and had practised on a regular basis for two nights a week in the Drill Hall. When the day arrived, they were reasonably confident that they would be able to compete with their colleagues from the other villages.

Mary was also looking forward to accompanying John for the weekend. She had never been away from her family in all the time that she had been married. Ellen and Margaret were taking over the running of the house for the weekend when their mother was away, and Mary felt confident that everything was in good hands.

The competitions were to be held in the large conference hall, where a realistic mock accident was enacted. The patients were actors, who were made up to look as realistic as possible. The make-up material for this process was developed by plastic surgeons during the World War. There was a time limit set for the completion of the test. Marks were awarded for efficiency, non-aggravation of injury, and the possibility of saving a patient's life. The company encouraged this type of competition because they believed that it was good training practice for the quick diagnosis and treatment of injuries, both at work and in everyday life.

Each village had to provide a judge. Creswell's entrant was Dr Wood.

The teams arrived on the Friday night and had a relaxing evening on the campus. John, Mary, Vic and his wife spent their night in the bar playing bridge and drinking beer. To Mary it seemed like something out of another world. She often went with her family to the village Institute, drank a couple of gills of ale and watched a turn on the stage – usually a singer or comic – and chattered away to her neighbours in a smoke-filled room which smelt continuously of stale beer; but to visit Edwinstow Hall was a luxury she had never known in all of her life.

'I think I'll stay 'ere fer a year, and let Ellen and Margaret look after the 'ouse,' Mary said to John when they were in bed. Quickly changing the subject, she continued, 'They must 'ave spent a fortune on this place!'

'It's very nice,' replied John as he looked around the room. 'There's one thing about Bolsover Colliery Company, they do think about their men sometimes; which is more then can be said fer some other owners. Mind you, they must use this place fer buyers and other visitors. It must give 'em a good impression ter come 'ere. Don't forget they're not only mine owners. They are involved in railways, and coal lorries like the Thomas Black

Company; and there's still a lot er coal goes abroad from our mines.'

Mary felt the white linen sheets and pillowcases. 'It's like bein' royalty. There's no expense spared on anythin',' she ventured.

'Yer'd think so if yer had ter wash 'em,' said John, laughing, 'and yer could spend a day er so sweepin' the carpets as well, if yer wanted somert ter pass yer time. At least yer wouldn't 'ave ter use soda and paraffin ter get shut er the insects, like yer do in the church 'alls!'

Mary propped her head on her hand and looked at her husband; 'It looks like all that practisin' yer spent on this could be worth while. If only it gets yer a trip like this every now and then,' she said hopefully.

'We'll see termorrow whether the practice was worth while,' said John as he kissed his wife on the forehead and turned out the light.

The following morning was bright and sunny. After breakfast the Saul family went for a walk in Sherwood Forest, before the big event.

'It reminds me of when I was young,' said John. 'Dad and me spent 'ours in the Doncaster wood.'

'That's where yer caught all them butterflies that er framed in the front room, didn't yer, Dad?' asked Walt as they rambled around the tree trunks.

'Yes,' said John, 'yer granddad used ter catch em with er net. I don't think there's as many types er butterfly in 'ere as there was in Doncaster. Mind you; it's a bit early in the year yet, ter really tell.'

'Do yer know what the accident ull be fer the competition, Dad?' asked Bill as he slowly walked down the pathway; he was feeling slightly nervous about having to perform the test in public.

John picked up a twig and broke it into two. 'I'm not sure, I asked Vic and he didn't know either. One thing's fer sure the team competition ull be somethin' in the mine. The individual test could be owt.'

Mary kicked at some dead foliage at the side of the footpath. 'Why don't yer ask Dr Wood if 'e knows what it is?' she asked.

Walter smiled at his mother and said, ''Es sure ter know, Mam; 'e's a judge; but 'e won't be allowed ter tell us because it would give us an advantage over the other teams in the competition.'

'I'm not so sure about that,' replied John, 'even if we did know it would be too late to do anythin' about it now. Ye'll either know it now or yer won't; it's as simple as that.'

They all returned to the main hall, had their lunch and made for the conference hall. Chairs had been placed around the side of the hall, for spectators to watch the performance of the teams, when they carried out their work in the middle of the room. Mary watched with interest, as the order for the teams were drawn out of a bag. She was personally proud to have three of her family in the competition. Mansfield 'A' colliery team was the first to go. Followed by Creswell 'A', John's team.

When John's team's turn arrived, they found, as expected, a mining scene in the centre of the room. They were given a card which gave the general outline to the mock accident. It read:

A young lad had led his pony with an empty tub to the coalface. The boy unhitched the animal from the tub and turned round and started to walk the pony back to collect another tub when he heard the cry of a man's voice. He looked round to see the body of a miner laid on his side, on the floor, propped up against the tub that the young lad had just unhitched from the pony. The man had been pulling at a rock – trying to move it – at the side of the rail track. The rock all of a sudden moved; the man fell backwards and pushed the empty tub forward; the tub then slid back and hit the man on the right side of his body. The youngster shouted for help from the other men on the coalface. When someone came to assist the injured man, the lad was told to run for the first aid kit. When the injured man was asked were he was hurt, the miner first mentioned his right arm, stating that any type of movement brought him pain. The injured man then turned on to his bottom and said that he had pains in his backside and hip when he moved.

John read the card and went into the middle of the room. An actor was made up for the part of the patient showing the following injuries:

A cut on his forehead about two inches long. There was a small amount of blood seeping from the wound.

The right humerus displayed an open fracture. The arm was very swollen. A small wound displaying a piece of broken bone on the surface; and there was a small haemorrhage from the injury.

There was also an impacted fracture on the socket joint of the right femur.

The bell rang and the Creswell team began. John put his hand gently on the patient's shoulder to give him reassurance, and told the man to lie still.

He asked the miner what had happened to cause the accident, where the patient was hurt, and if he felt any pain.

The first injury John noted was the cut on the forehead. The ostler turned to Vic and pointed to the cut. 'See ter that will yer,' he told him.

Vic made a general inspection of the face to ensure that there were no fractures. He then applied pressure to the wound and continued to hold the cut until it had stopped bleeding. Vic then applied a padding directly on the forehead, and firmly bandaged around the head.

'I'll check that the bleedin's controlled before we put him on the stretcher,' said Vic, and looked up at the judge, who just nodded.

Meanwhile John had continued to examine the patient's right arm, and gave Walt the problem of dealing with the limb.

Walter gave an immediate support to the arm, by holding it firmly. He found out by gently feeling the patient's shirtsleeve that it was sticky and damp. The limb was very tender and it was swollen. Walt ripped open the shirtsleeve to find a small wound, from which was protruding a small piece of bone. He quickly examined the rest of the arm for any further injury while he continued to support the injured limb. Walter opened a sterile dressing and applied it to the injured portion of the arm. He built up the dressing with padding.

Walt then wrapped the padding, injury, and arm together with a diagonal bandage. The patient's forearm was then placed across his chest, just touching the opposite armpit. Soft padding was placed between the injured man's chest and arm to avoid chafing. The arm was then supported by making a triangular bandage into a sling. A broad bandage was tied round the sling, helping to secure the upper part of the limb. Finally Walt checked the man's pulse.

While Walter was dealing with the patient's arm, John had continued his inspection further down the miner's body; and he asked Bill to attend to the first aid on the patient's right leg.

Bill enthusiastically set about his task. When his patient complained of pain, Bill immediately supported the injured leg with his hand, as he continued his examination of the limb. Bill found that there was tenderness and swelling at the top of the leg, and assumed that there could be an impacted fracture of the femur, but he continued to examine the rest of the limb for any further damage. Next, he brought the sound limb very gently to the side of the injured leg and applied some soft padding between the two limbs.

Bill then placed a long padded splint to the side of the damaged limb. The splint extended from the armpit to the right foot. He then secured the splint with broad bandages around the chest, pelvis, thighs, legs, knees, ankles and feet. All of the bandages were then checked by another member of the team for correct tightness.

While the rest of the team carried out their tasks, John fully examined the patient's left side. He checked the patient's pulse, and the paleness of the skin, making observations on the coldness, or clamminess, of the epidermis to the touch. When all the work was completed, blankets and pillows were utilised for the comfort and warmth of the patient. The injured man was then placed on a stretcher and strapped in a Lowmoor Jacket – an implement that secures the patient on a stretcher and allows him to be placed in an upright position, if necessary. The stretcher was then placed on a tub and slowly wheeled out of the mine. John went to the judge and informed him that the doctor and ambulance had been notified on the surface, by one of the haulage workers when delivering coal out of the mine.

Each member of the team were also required to carry out an individual test. Walt was drawn to go first; the information given to him was written on a card as follows:

> You are walking down a gateway – a road – towards the working face of a mine, when a man comes staggering towards you. He is complaining of a headache, dizziness and feeling weak. When you speak to the miner his judgement seems impaired and he is very uncooperative.

The bell rang for Walter to start his examination. A 'miner' came staggering towards him. Walt asked his patient if he was injured in any way. The man complained about headaches, dizziness and fatigue. Walter tried to walk the man towards the first aid post but he was uncooperative. Walt looked at the judge and said, 'The man seems ter be gassed in some way. 'E's possibly got carbon-monoxide poisoning.' He collected a stretcher from the side of the hall, laid his patient on it, and covered him with blankets. He then asked an assistant to give him a hand to carry the man out of the mine as quickly as possible, and out into the fresh air.

Other individual tests for the rest of the Creswell team included a bursting varicose vein, a fractured kneecap and a man suffering from shock.

The winners of the team prize were from Bolsover Colliery; Creswell's 'A' team came second. John asked the judges where they had lost marks and was told that on occasions some of the bandaging was a bit slack and they were too long in carrying out their work. However, Walter won the individual prize for his quick recognition that his patient had carbon-monoxide poisoning. Mary proudly kept the silver cup on the sideboard in her front room after she had shown the trophy to all her neighbours and friends.

*

By the year 1925, Joe was not the only business in Duchess Street. At number 21 Edward Hughes had set up as an insurance agent. He had persuaded Mary to take out two penny policies on the death of her husband. However insurance was an expense that John felt was totally unnecessary; even though he had seen several widows with families in a destitute state after the loss of the home's breadwinner, and unable to pay the funeral expenses.

Joseph Wood at twenty-three had opened a confectionery shop. His stocks included many types of toffee, e.g. walnut, treacle, cinder and chocolate-topped. He also sold boiled sweets, acid drops, jelly babies, wine gums, liquorice allsorts, coconut slices, coconut chips, tiger nuts, aniseed balls, candy rock, marshmallows, chocolate bars, walnut whirls and hundreds and thousands. Joseph also kept many types of children's sweets which allowed the youngsters to spend their halfpennies and pennies. These items included gobstoppers, hearts and crosses, everlasting sticks, sugared mice, sugared tobacco, sweet cigarettes, liquorice pipes, sherbet dips and lucky bags.

Joseph Wood also sold various kinds of tobaccos, including, Virginia dark, Virginia light, Gold Flake and Twist. Cigarettes included Woodbines, Player's Weight and Gold Tip. He also sold Havana cigars and many types of smokers' requisites such as pipes, cigarette holders and tobacco pouches.

William Greaves at number 37 was a shopkeeper selling mainly groceries. His stocks included sides of bacon hung from nails in the roof in his storeroom, barrels of butter, hundredweight bags of sugar and flour, barrels of currants and raisins, large slabs of butter and lard, and wooden crates full of tea. All of the produce was weighed out into the required portions at the back of the shop. Other groceries included various tinned products; for example, cocoa, baked beans and different fruits. There were many jars of produce, including coffee and jam. Bottled cordials included orange, dandelion and burdock and lemonade.

Another shop that the Saul family traded with was the herbalist John Dooley at number 17, Moran Street. Mary's mother made many of these products and she had full belief in their effectiveness. The products were made from herbs such as; aniseed, balm, bay leaf, borage, caraway, chives, cinnamon, cloves nutmeg, rosemary and many more. Mr Dooley also sold many varieties of home-made wine; including agrimony, clover, parsley, beetroot, potato, apple, elderberry, elderflower, gooseberry and blackberry. Each wine he believed had medicinal properties and was a cure for a specific ailment.

Mary also made up her own concoctions from the herbs like thyme, parsley and sage which John grew in the allotment. Home-made products that she utilised, which she believed were for the health of her children, included rubbing goose grease on their chest in the middle of winter to prevent colds; taking brimstone and treacle, which she helped down with a spoonful of sugar, and hot blackberry vinegar – heated with a hot poker – for sweating out any flu symptoms.

There were also several hawkers who traded round the village streets. Harold Hazelby from Elmton Road delivered milk on his horse and cart. The milk was stored in shiny metal containers from which he measured out gills of the liquid and ladled it into the householders' own containers that they brought into the street on the arrival of the cart.

The infamous rag-and-bone man always made his weekly rounds. He often exchanged sweets with the children for a small rag, or an occasional rabbit skin.

The children's favourite hawker was Sami Saddel, the hokey-pokey ice-cream man who delivered his produce on a bike. The ice cream was made from cornflower, milk, and ice that was delivered by train from Grimsby.

Sami and John were good friends and often discussed their different types of work. Sami knew that John was interested in history; and one day he explained to the ostler the beginnings of the ice-cream trade. This was the hokey's explanation of how his trade was born.

The Emperor Nero was believed to be the first person to produce ice-cream products around AD 62. He sent fast runners from his palace to the nearby peaks of the Apennines to bring back snow, which he flavoured with milk and honey.

In the thirteenth century Marco Polo, the Venetian explorer, brought back many priceless jewels from the Orient. But he also obtained a formula for a frozen milk dish which was similar to sherbet. The first ice cream made in England was believed to be about the time of the American Revolution.

Jacob Fussel, a Baltimore (American) milkman, was the first man to establish an ice-cream plant in 1851. Ice-cream cones were first served in St Louis in 1904.

Chapter Ten

The General Strike

Between May and November 1924, over one hundred mines were closed in Great Britain. There was a general decline in the world trade for coal, and other sources of energy were being developed. The miners' unions were also concerned about the amount of reparation coal that Germany was supplying to other countries in payment for war damage; this was affecting British exports.

When Baldwin became Prime Minister in December 1924, he appointed Winston Churchill as the Chancellor of the Exchequer. In his budget of April 1925, Churchill, on the advice of some experts, announced that sterling (the British currency) would return to what was termed the gold standard. This meant that the value of the country's money would return to its pre-war value. The immediate effect was that the value of sterling was raised by ten per cent abroad; however, the purchasing power of money at home was to remain the same. This deliberate government policy caused many problems to our exporters. The Government was warned by many experts that wages would have to be cut by around ten per cent to compensate for the value of the pound in foreign countries, causing a large drop in living standards for many workers in Britain; but the warnings were ignored.

The gold standard for the mine owners who exported coal meant a reduction of one shilling and ninepence a ton in order to compete with other countries in the open market. However in many of the inefficient mines the profit they were making was only sixpence a ton. The only way that the owner could bridge the gap was to reduce the employees' wages.

The miners had to suffer the consequences of a government policy for which they were not responsible. When other factors were included, such as, thousands of unemployed miners seeking work, and the inefficiency of many of the British mines in comparison to other countries, the only solution was a drastic reduction in the standard of living for many miners in numerous parts of the country.

At the end of June 1925 the mine owners terminated their agreement with their employees, and arranged for discussions with the unions about new contracts for the workers, because of the change in the value of sterling. The owners wanted a large reduction in wages, ranging from nine per cent to forty-eight per cent depending on the district in which the mine was located; and an increase in working hours from seven to eight hours a day.

The unions unanimously rejected the owners' offer, insisting that there should be no reduction in pay for the members, or increases in hours worked.

The owners issued lockout notices for 31st July, 1925. However, to avoid a major confrontation in the mining industry, the Government provided a subsidy for the mine owners until a public inquiry had taken place.

Many union delegates on the left were trying to convert the crisis into a revolution, whereas others on the right were taking a step backwards from a conflict with the established powers.

In the Saul family, Margaret left school at Christmas in 1924 and went to work in service at Stockport; and Ellen had her first child, a boy called Desmond, early in 1922.

Unfortunately the miners' problem was not solved by a public inquiry, and in the middle of April 1926 most of the mine owners in Britain gave their workers notice that their contracts of employment where to be terminated on 30th April. This was not carried out by the owners in Nottinghamshire.

William was once again in conversation with John at the Saul's family home in Duke Street after another union meeting.

'Bring a chair up ter the fire,' said John and pointed to the chair at the side of the kitchen table as William came into the room. 'Are we on the brink of disaster again then?'

'It looks that way, John,' replied William as he sat by the glowing fire. 'Once again we seem ter be in a situation where we are just keepin' faith with the union at the national level, with nothin' in it fer us.'

'Why don't they do some talkin', instead er just arguin' all the time? They're like two bulls wi' their 'orns locked together; no one seems ter be budgin' an inch.'

'That's true, but there's some large principles at stake 'ere,' replied William defensively.

'Yer can't eat principles,' replied John in an agitated voice. 'What are the union really askin' fer now?'

'The same as they wanted from the beginnin',' replied William as he leaned back in his chair. 'They want no decrease in wages; no increase in 'ours of work and wage negotiations at national level.

'The owners want exactly the opposite, ter compensate fer the loss in the value of the pound that's affected their profits, with wage negotiations at district levels.'

'There's no wonder the bloody talkin's deadlocked,' said John sadly, 'but someone's got ter shift their stance or we could be on strike fer ever! If we could negotiate wi' our own owners, they would sort it out before the strike could begin.'

William smiled at his father-in-law. 'The unions won't let us make an agreement locally. What they are tryin' ter do is ter stop the supply of coal fer the whole country. They're afraid that Notts might make a district agreement like they did in the lockout of 1893. If they did, a strike in the rest er the country would be a waste er time.'

★

On 30th April, 1926 nearly every mine in the country was closed down. The Nottinghamshire miners were out on strike, once again to keep faith with their less fortunate colleagues. Neither the union nor mine owners would budge an inch. The trade union movement believed that to reduce the wages of the miners was a forerunner to cutting the wages in every industry in the country. The TUC (Trades Union Council) agreed to give the miners any assistance that they required to reach a satisfactory solution to their problem.

The TUC Executive met for three days at the end of April and decided to arrange a general strike (this was a false name for the strike, because only selected workers would be called out on strike by the unions) in sympathy with the miners, if a satisfactory agreement could not be reached between the miners, colliery owners and the Government.

The workers who were to be called out if the strike was to be implemented would include: transport workers, printers, iron and steal, metal, chemical, builders, electricity and gas workers. However, employees in the food trade were allowed to stay at work.

On Sunday 2nd May the TUC met the Prime Minister. The negotiators came to an agreement without the miners' leaders, who were late for the meeting because they had all been in their own districts. However, Baldwin was informed that the *Daily Mail* workers had refused to print an article that described the strike as revolutionary; and he cut off the negotiations. Some of the Cabinet ministers wanted a showdown with the unions and believed that the time had now come for action.

Although it was the last thing that the TUC wanted, and had done everything in their power to stop, they had no option but to arrange a general strike. The strike began on Tuesday 4th May, 1926.

During the following week a draft proposal was put forward. The TUC believed that the terms in the draft was a basis for the settlement of the miners' dispute, and decided to call off the general strike on 12th May. The TUC met the Prime Minister and told them of their decision. Baldwin promised to do all in his power to find a fair and lasting settlement for all parties involved.

The miners' union would not accept any agreement which included a reduction in pay, or increased hours of work for their members. They rejected the draft proposals and remained on strike. They also believed that they had been let down by other unions in the dispute.

Because of the three earlier strikes in the Twenties, the Nottinghamshire union was nearly broke when they became involved in the 1926 dispute. It was not until

March 1926 that the debts incurred by the earlier strikes had been paid off. Creswell miners were only paid a few shillings a month strike pay. The union could not use the food coupon system that they utilised in an earlier strike, because they were very slow to pay the shopkeepers their money that was owing to them. The stores were unwilling to participate in a similar scheme again. Also, many appeals that were made for help from the general public was very muted during the early stages of the strike.

George Spencer, a Nottinghamshire union delegate, suggested at the national union conference in the middle of May that the Notts area was in financial difficulties and should be given a larger share of the funds that were paid out at national level in order to assist the Notts miners. However, this suggestion was rejected by the other districts.

There was a fear in the national union that the Notts miners would be the weak link in the chain. Several times in the recent past they had supported their colleagues in other districts with no benefit to themselves. There was a general apathy among the Notts miners towards the strike. The Creswell colliers could have remained at work on their old rates of pay because of the efficiency of their own mine.

Two mines in Nottinghamshire, Blidworth and Clipstone, worked through the dispute with the blessing of the union, because they were new mines and classed as developing pits. To add to the union's problems, the Notts colliery owners were continuously encouraging the miners to break away from the national union. They had not terminated the workers' contracts, as had occurred in other mining districts, and they were hoping for a local settlement with their employees.

★

At the beginning of June 1926, John, Walt and Bill came home from a union meeting. Mary was seated at the kitchen table peeling potatoes. Peggy, Agnus and Cath were sat by the side of the hearth playing cards. The three men looked grim faced. John took off his overcoat and flat cap and hung it behind the kitchen door. He turned to the girls and told them, 'Get yer coats on, you three, yer've got ter go down ter the Methodist 'All on Mansfield Road, and take some jugs wi' yer.'

Mary turned and looked at her husband in shock. 'What's goin' on, John?' she asked.

John sadly bent his head. 'They're settin' up two soup kitchens; one's at the Drill Hall and the other at the Methodist Chapel, fer all the kids in the village whose fathers are on strike,' he replied.

John, Mary, Bill and Walt watched the girls go out of the door. Mary hung her head and gave a large sigh, 'It's come ter somert when we start wi' soup kitchens. I can remember when I was a kid that we did that; I always 'oped that my family wouldn't 'ave ter go through that,' she said gloomily.

John twitched his moustache and looked at Bill and Walt, 'I must say it is degradin', if not demoralising, when yer can't feed yer own family. At least there's only three of 'em ter worry about now,' he replied. 'In a couple er months there'll be stuff ready in the allotment. But fer the time bein' were just goin' ter 'ave ter swallow our pride and let the girls go ter the 'alls. At least they'll 'ave somert ter eat.'

'I suppose yer right,' said Mary sadly with her head bowed low. 'It still takes money, though, ter set up and run them soup kitchens. I wonder where they got it from.'

Bill looked at his mother's dejected face and limp body.

'Apparently there was an appeal in the Nottingham Journal fer meals fer miners' children and their dependants, and they've got er big response. As Dad says, Mam, at least the girls ull 'ave somert ter eat. We can manage a bit better than them. They're not ter blame fer the problems in the mines,' he offered.

'It's the Government's ter blame,' replied Walt. 'If they 'ad not set up this stupid gold standard it would never 'ave 'appened.'

'There's lots er people ter blame,' interrupted John, 'but the fact still remains that it's 'appened. We can't do much about it; and fer the time bein' we 'ave ter live we it.'

About an hour later the girls came bursting in the back door, took off their overcoats, and rushed to tell their parents, who were both sitting around the kitchen table, what had happened.

'Steady on, and catch yer breath!' Mary spoke calmly to her three panting daughters, who seemed to be splitting at the seams to give their parents the information. 'What did they give yer ter eat?'

It was Peggy who answered first as the girls put the full jugs on the table, 'There was some meat soup – at least I think it was meat – but it was very weak,' she said.

'It looks like dishwatter,' butted in Agnus.

'Shut up a minute while a tell Mam,' retorted Peggy. 'At least it's wet and warm, and they gave us a couple er slices er bread ter go wi' it.' The young girl held out a paper bag with the bread in it. 'It isn't bad, it tastes all right, anyway.'

'We've got some custard, rice puddin' and prunes as well,' said Cath, 'and it's all lumpy!'

John looked sadly at his three daughters, 'At least yer've got somethin' ter eat,' he said. ''Ave they told yer ter go back?'

'Yes!' replied Peggy. 'We'll 'ave ter go back every day about twelve o'clock, when the meals 'ave been cooked.'

'Was there many at the 'all?' asked Mary.

'It was packed out; there was a big queue right through the door,' replied Agnus, 'I didn't think that there was so many kids in the village.'

During the strike many of the tradesmen gave groceries and milk to help to feed the miners' children but it only scratched the surface of the problem, as the weeks stretched into months. Fortunately the summer of 1926 provided mainly fine weather. John occupied most of his time in the allotment and he daily checked the health of the ponies who were happily grazing in a field at the back of the mine. Bill and Walt collected lumps of coal from the railway lines, including the disused line in the Grips, near Clowne town, that used to come from the old Clowne colliery in the late nineteenth century.

One day near the end of June, John came home from the allotment at the same time that Bill and Walter had returned from the village.

'Anythin' 'appenin' down there? Any excitement ter make life interestin'?' he asked.

'There's plenty er police about as usual,' Walter answered his father's question. 'It makes yer wonder what they normally do when the strike's not on. There's lots er men and gaffers playin' cards together fer matchsticks. As usual, there's men stood around talkin' about the rights and wrongs er the strike.'

'One er two of 'em are walkin' the streets lookin' fer tab ends fer a quick drag er two,' put in Bill. 'There's men stood outside the pub waitin' and 'opin' fer a free drink. I don't think that I've ever seen so many people looking so dejected in me life.'

John looked at the sad faces of his two sons, and told them, 'It's as yer Mam says: God works in mysterious ways; only 'E knows best; but sometimes yer do 'ave ter wonder what the point of it all is. One things fer sure, it won't get any better until the pit wheels start ter turn again; and even then it's goin' ter take er lot er gettin' over this strike.'

'They reckon that a lot er miners in Notts are workin' privately on the outcrops,' said Bill, 'and the unions are gettin' worried about it.'

'I'm not surprised,' answered John. 'The unions called the strike, they give the men a pittance in strike pay, and they expect the men ter be loyal. But when yer've got a family, yer've got a loyalty ter them as well. There's nowt worse fer a man then ter see 'is wife and kids wi' empty bellies and ragged clothes.'

★

By the end of July only a small number of miners were at work in the Notts county, around seven hundred; most of these were working at the new Clipstone (Clipstone was a Bolsover company mine) and Blidworth pits; however many were working full-time on outcrops.

On 19th August, 1926 many of the union branch members, including those from Creswell, held a meeting with the directors of The Bolsover Colliery Company at Edwinstow Hall.

About a week later the Creswell union organised a meeting of their members at the local cinema on King's Street, The Electric Palace. The picture house was full of miners (many were not able to get in) with all the local union delegates sitting on the stage, including Horace Carter the secretary and Harry Tracey the treasurer. The delegates explained to their audience that the union's National Executive's position had not changed since the beginning of the strike; and went on to tell their members about the meeting at Edwinstow Hall with the mine owners the previous week. The mine owners had offered the men ninety per cent of the wage they were receiving before the strike started; and the miners would have to work an extra half-hour a day. These conditions were the owners offer if the men wished to return to work.

There was a numbed silence in the cinema, for about a minute. Then one of the miners, Fred Clark, walked on to the stage and said, 'Yer can do what yer like, but I'm goin' back. I've an 'ungry family ter feed.'

There was uproar in the cinema, as Fred walked out of the door, followed by three other men. However, it was the start of the return to work for many of the other miners in the days to come. Many had exhausted their savings, sold some of their furniture and pawned their best clothes; and often they were in fear of eviction from their homes for not being able to pay their rents. There was great pressure from their wives and children to go back to work.

In the middle of August 1926, George Spencer – one of the Nottinghamshire union delegates – told the national conference that the Notts miners would prefer a national wage settlement. However three days later, the mine owners once again refused to negotiate nationally, and had insisted on local agreements with their employees.

At the beginning of September 1926, there were believed to be over seven thousand miners back at work in Nottinghamshire. A large majority of these were Bolsover Colliery Company workers – there was probably between sixty per cent and seventy per cent of the Creswell miners back at work in the first week of September. It now seemed impossible for the Notts union officials to prevent some sort of breakaway movement.

Creswell colliery was the first pit in the country to bring out coal after the 1926 miners' strike.

John had returned to work in the interest of the ponies and Walt and Bill had followed their father back to the mine.

By the end of September probably eighteen thousand miners were at work in the Notts district.

In many of the Notts collieries, miners coming into the county from outside towns and villages and were taking the local workers' jobs. In Creswell, miners came from Wales, Durham and Northumberland. They were all attempting to find work in the village mine.

The problem of outsiders taking locals' work came to a head at the beginning of October, when the miners at Digby colliery voted to go back to work. They asked George Spencer, the district union delegate, to arrange a meeting with the mine owners and make an agreement that all of the local men who had been on strike, and had been loyal to the union, should have their own jobs back for an undertaking that there would be a full return to work.

Up to this time George Spencer had held the official line. But he agreed to his members' request and successfully negotiated the miners' jobs back; and protected their livelihoods, which would have been lost to outsiders who were looking for work in the Nottinghamshire villages. The following day Spencer was approached by seven other local miners' union delegates, asking him to approach their owners to negotiate a return to work. This he was able to accomplish.

A week later Spencer was ordered to a special national conference in London to explain his action. He told the delegates that the managers of the mines were refusing to set men back on who had been loyal to the union all through the strike, and they were employing strangers in their place. He told the conference that he believed that he had acted in the best interest of the union members. The only repayment the miners would have got for loyalty to the union was the loss of their own jobs. Spencer told the delegates that he believed that he had done the best days work in his life by protecting his members' jobs.

Spencer was told to leave the conference and was regarded as a blackleg. By safeguarding the Notts miners jobs, he had lost everything that he had fought for all of his life. About a week later Spencer was suspended by the Notts union. This made him very bitter and he was determined to form an alternative union in the Nottinghamshire district.

On the last day of October 1926, delegates of the Notts branches who were at work – including Creswell – held a meeting in Mansfield and invited George Spencer to attend. At the meeting the union officials asked Spencer to meet the colliery owners and negotiate new contracts for their members. A meeting was arranged for the following week, when Spencer negotiated new contracts for all of the miners whose delegates had been at the original meeting.

The delegates accepted the terms and advised their members to sign the new agreement as quickly as possible. Spencer formed a new union and called it, The Nottinghamshire and District Mines Union, which came to be known as, The Spencer Union. The Spencer Union was a non-political union. The nucleus of the new union was formed from companies who utilised the butty system, including The Bolsover Colliery Company.

All of the Creswell miners had to join the new union.

Around the middle of November 1926, around forty-four thousand of the fifty-one thousand colliers in Nottinghamshire were thought to be back at work.

In the middle of December the mine owners in Nottinghamshire confirmed that they would only recognise the Spencer Union in their collieries. So began a division of the Notts union which was to last for twelve years.

Around the middle of November, at a national miners' conference, the union delegates were instructed that all districts were to negotiate terms of employment at district level: *the miners were beaten*. By the beginning of December all the British miners were back at work on the owners' terms.

The most disastrous trade union dispute in British industrial history had come to an end.

Part Four

The Changing Years

Chapter Eleven

Joe's Shops

The expected rise in demand for coal after the general strike did not materialise. In fact the demand for the hard black mineral decreased. A voluntary system was set up between the colliery owners which came into operation in 1928, whereby each mine produced a quota of coal that was based on the mines previous five years' production.

The Bolsover Colliery Co. opened Thoresby colliery, their sixth, and last mine, in 1928. Thoresby was one of the first all-electric collieries, which showed how progressive the company was in their working activities. However it was one of the last mines to be opened in Nottinghamshire until the Second World War in 1939.

Many advances were made in the efficiency of Creswell colliery and included the introduction of the first electric coal cutter in 1925.

By 1928 there was a regular motor bus service into Creswell that ran to and from Clowne, Staveley, Chesterfield and Doncaster. The postal service provided by the post office was sent through Mansfield.

There was a large increase of around forty new commercial properties in the village between 1924–28, following the building of the China Town housing estate at the top of Elmton Road. There was also a larger variety of businesses by 1928 including a china shop, a specialised fruiterer, a milliner, a furnisher, a carter, a picture frame maker, a wallpaper shop, a decorator, dentists, baker and the Pleasley Co-op.

In the Saul family, Peggy left school in 1927 and went into service at Stockport. Ellen now had three children, Desmond, Eric and Iris. However the biggest change came when Joe bought a shop on Elmton Road which he opened as a bicycle sales and repair shop. The whole family went to live at the back of the shop. Joe later opened a shop at 125 Welbeck Street where the family of his new wife, Rose Turner, ran the business.

The first bikes to be made were probably made with wooden wheels and they may have been propelled like a scooter.

Karl Saurerbon patented the first two-wheeled riding machine in 1817. The vehicle consisted of two wheels of equal size, with heavy iron spokes, connected to a bar. A seat was connected to the bar. The machine was propelled by the rider pushing his or her feet along the ground. A London coachmaker, Denis Johnson, produced a similar type of bike to Saurerbon's; however, the rider was able to steer his version of the cycle.

The first bike with pedals was attributed to Kirkpatrick Macmillan, a Dumfries blacksmith. Macmillan's cycle may have been the first machine that was able to be driven forward without the driver's feet having to touch the ground during his journey.

A Frenchman, Pierre Michaux, was the first known manufacturer and retailer of bikes. His products were exported to England around 1867. There were various types of bike manufactures in England from 1868 onwards. The major producers were found around Coventry, Birmingham and London.

During the 1870s cycling clubs became very popular. Many clubs had their own uniform and the groups were very clannish. The first recorded cycle track race was at St Cloud near Paris in 1868. The first known cycle race in England was on Whit Monday, 1868. The first cycle race in the Olympic Games was in 1896.

There were many gradual improvements in the design and quality of bikes. One innovation was the Ordinary Cycle, or penny-farthing, which was popular between 1870 and 1892. There were many designs and manufactures of this type of two-wheeled vehicle.

The safety-designed bike, the type seen today, was first made in 1869, but did not gain popularity until the late 1880s. From 1902 this type of frame was the one that was exclusively used by all manufacturers.

An important development in bicycles occurred in 1888 when John Boyd Dunlop invented the pneumatic tyre – a tyre containing wind or gas. By 1892 all the major bike manufacturers used the blow up tyre on their machines.

Until the late 1890s the bike lamps were nearly all oil lamps of various types. After that time a dynamo lamp was introduced.

From 1902 the majority of bikes were fitted with a free wheel; all cycles were painted black.

*

One Monday afternoon early in January 1927, John and Mary were sat drinking a cup of tea and watching their oldest son who was repairing a chain on a man's bike, when Joe looked up to his mother and said, 'What would yer think about the idea er moving from 'ere and goin' ter live on Elmton Road, Mam? There's a shop up there I'd like ter rent.'

Mary looked at her son in shock. 'I'm not really sure that I would like ter leave this 'ouse ter be 'onest. We've lived 'ere now fer nearly twenty-five years; we've 'ad our ups and downs, but in the main it's been a lucky 'ome. All of the family but you and Ellen were born in this 'ouse and it 'as a lot er memories, both good and bad, in it,' she answered.

'What are yer thinkin' about son?' asked John quizzically as he gave a side glance at his wife.

Joe continued to repair the bike chain without looking at his parents. 'I've been lookin' at an empty shop across from the Model,' he said. 'There's too much work now ter do it properly in this small room; we can't expand any more in this 'ouse, and when I get married next month there's not goin' ter be much room 'ere. I would probably get more trade up there, and we would all be better off. I could sell bikes; there'd be more room ter do the repairs; there's more 'ouse space; and there's only the two girls now that Peggy's gone ter Stockport.'

John looked thoughtfully at his son. 'Yer know a lot er families in the village are still tryin' ter get over the strike and most er the men er on short time. It's a bit of er gamble ter take that on in terday's world,' he told him.

'Everythin' in life's a gamble, Dad,' replied Joe as he put the repaired chain back on the bike. 'But yer 'ave ter speculate ter accumulate; and there's only one way ter find out!'

'What about the rent?' asked Mary. 'It'll be a good amount if the shop's where I think it is; and there'll be a lot er other expenses that yer've never ever thought about.'

Joe stood up and straightened his back. 'I've looked inter that. The rent's forty-five pounds a year and then there's the rates. It's more money then we're payin' for rent 'ere – and yer'd expect it ter be – but the extra trade will make up the difference and should easily cover any extra expenses. It should be better all round then struggling on 'ere.'

John looked at Mary, who seemed slightly perplexed. He told Joe, 'I would give it a couple er days ter think it over, son. If yer think it's right after that; and yer want ter try; there's no 'arm in 'avin' a go ter see what yer can do. The Sauls 'ave been in business fer hundreds er years, so it's in yer blood. But I do share yer Mam's concern about the project, especially as the work is at the moment in the pit. And I do feel a kind er sadness about leavin' 'ere, because we've brought yer all up in this 'ouse.'

In the middle of March 1927, John borrowed a horse and cart from one of the coal merchants who traded at the colliery and the Sauls went to live in their new abode.

Joe's shop on Elmton Road was facing the bottom of the Model, and was in a group of five shops including John Lockwood who repaired watches and clocks; John Belfield, a butcher; Arthur Birch, who sold fish and chips; and William Harper – his shop was on the corner of Ann's Street – who was a confectioner.

In the new shop Joe sold and repaired bikes. There were many manufactures of bikes including Raleigh, Rudge, Whitworth, Royal Enfield and Hercules. Cycles from all of the manufactures had become a more stereotyped machine. The wheels were either twenty-six or twenty-eight inches in diameter, and they were wide and thick (some racers had a twenty-seven-inch diameter wheel). Chromium plating had replaced nickel as the metal used on wheels and handlebars, and celluloid was utilised to manufacture mudguards and chain guards.

Cycles were very reasonably priced and very popular in the late Twenties and Thirties, and they were the main means of transport, apart from walking, for the working people. Joe obtained a dealership for the Hercules cycles, a very popular make around that time. They were manufactured by a British company in Birmingham.

One of Joe's first customers for new bikes was John's friend Vic Jones. Joe, with the assistance of Walt, was trying to display four new bikes in the shop window when Vic walked through the door.

'It's nice ter see all these willin' workers,' said the miner, and smiled at the two Saul brothers. 'I was lookin' in the window and thought that I might buy me two grandkids a bike fer their birthday in June. There's a boy and er girl.'

'Yer've come ter the right place, Vic,' replied Joe as he ran over his own foot with one of the new bikes. 'Just look at these four smashin' new 'Ercules. There's two lady's and two gent's – one straight 'andlebar and one racer fer each sex – that are well worth 'avin'. I would buy 'em meself, so I've no problem in tryin' ter sell 'em ter you.'

'They look pretty good ter me; but I'm not an expert in bikes,' replied Vic as he rubbed his hands over one of the handlebars.

Going into his sales patter, Joe explained the quality of the bikes. 'Yer can see the difference between the two types: the racer 'as the rounded down chromium 'andlebars and the others 'ave straight chromium 'andlebars. The racers 'ave Sturmey-Archer three-speed gears, but all the bikes 'ave the same accessories, including chromium wheels, a steel frame, Dunlop saddle and tyres, a bell, tool bag, oil can, a pump and pump clips.'

'I like the look of 'em, but what about the cost?' asked Vic cautiously.

Collecting his advertisement book from the counter, Joe showed Vic the prices, saying, 'The straight 'andle gent's bike would cost three pounds, nineteen and ninepence, or could be bought on 'ire-purchase at two shillings a week. A gent's racer, with Sturmey-Archer three-speed gears and rounded down handlebars costs four pounds, nine and sixpence. A lady's bike could be purchased for four pounds, five and ninepence, and a lady's racer for four pounds, seven and sixpence. They all could be bought on 'ire-puchase.'

Vic looked at the bikes for about a minute. 'I'll have one lady's and one gent's straight 'andlebars on HP,' he said. 'If they want ter go any quicker they'll 'ave ter pedal a bit faster; they've got plenty er energy ter burn away. But – as I told yer when I came in the shop – it's not their birthday until June. Can yer 'old em till then? I'll sign the agreement now though, and I can start payin' on 'em.

'That'll be okay, Vic,' said Joe. 'We'll make the HP forms out and yer can sign 'em.'

'Me misses says I'm as soft as a brush, wi' the grandkids,' replied his friend. 'But I get as much pleasure outer buyin' things fer 'em, as they do outer usin' em. See yer later, lads.' Vic waved his arm as he went out of the shop.

Two weeks later Joe went into John Belfield's shop to collect a pound of shin of beef that his mother had ordered. While he was waiting in the queue, Joe watched John's son walking out of the door to deliver an order. 'I've had an advertisement fer a shop bike come through the post terday, John, and it would suit you down ter the ground,' he told the butcher.

John Belfield looked at his neighbour suspiciously, 'I could do wi' a shop bike, but they're a bit expensive.'

'Not this one, John!' exclaimed Joe. 'I'll go and get the advertisement papers and yer can 'ave a look at 'em.' Joe rushed out of the door, but quickly returned with the leaflets.

John looked at the advertisement and raised his eyebrows as he read the information: a Raleigh butcher's bike, which the makers claimed could stand the weight of ten men, contained a basket with a girded front fork and was constructed with an all-steel frame. The cost was nine pounds and ten shillings, or seventeen shillings and ninepence a month.

'It looks a useful tool ter me, Joe. Yer can order one and we'll see what it looks like. But I'm not makin' any promises,' said the butcher, impressed.

'That's okay, John,' replied Joe cheerfully, 'we can always display it in the shop, or send back if it's no good.'

Two weeks later the bike arrived. Mr Belfield was pleased with the machine and became the proud owner of a new butcher's shop bike.

*

For both Agnus and Cath, 1927 was an important time in their young Christian lives, because on Easter Sunday they received their first Holy Communion. From the beginning of the year Father Macfaith had given the Catholic children in the village extra tuition on the catechism, to prepare them for their important day. Their full preparation began in Lent and both girls had decided to give up sweets as a penance, and put the money into the church collections.

Before Lent began, there was Shrove Tuesday, or Pancake Day, which was one of the Sauls special family days. The word *shrove* originates from word *shrive* from the time of the middle ages, and was a day of preparation for the season of Lent. The earliest pancakes were made because; the eating of eggs and fat were forbidden foods during the forty days of fasting and penitence which started the following day, Ash Wednesday.

Shrove Tuesday was a day that Mary and the girls always enjoyed, when the old large china water jug, belonging to John's parents, was put to good use. Milk, eggs and plain flour were whisked together to produce a thick, creamy frothy mixture. A large iron frying pan was filled with the fluid mixture and fried on the open fire. Mary's face was always flushed by the heat from the close contact with the fire. All the family laughed and danced as they each waited their turn for a fried pancake to be dished out of the massive cooking utensil for their dinner.

The next day, Ash Wednesday, Cath and Agnus went to Holy Mass. In the middle of service they joined the queue to the altar; where they knelt in front of the priest who made a sign of the cross on their foreheads with ashes produced from burning the palms that were left over from last year's Palm Sunday service. The grey cross was always worn with pride by the young children who seemed to consider it a badge. This was the start of forty days of agony, the period in which the two girls would be deprived of their sweets.

For a Catholic family, every Friday was a day of abstinence from eating meat; and fish was always on the menu for the main meal of the day. But this seemed to be of greater significance during the season of Lent.

Mothering Sunday was the middle Sunday in Lent. The children made Mary a card, and they cooked the Sunday lunch; allowing their mother to put her feet up for a whole day.

On Palm Sunday, one week before Easter Sunday, the mass began with a small procession; and at the end of the service the priest handed out palms from the Holy Land that were shaped in the form of a cross.

All of the Saul family went to church on Good Friday and said the Stations of the Cross. This was the only day of the year when a mass was never said by the priest.

Easter Saturday was the day when Agnus and Cath made their first act of confession. Agnus was first to go into the dark confessional, which consisted of a large box partitioned into two, with the priest on one side and a member of the church congregation on the other.

Agnus walked into the confessional box, closed the door and knelt on a cushion that was facing the side of the box where the priest sat. The child began, 'Bless me, Father, for I 'ave sinned.' Then she stopped and thought for a few moments.

Father Macfaith sat patiently in his chair and encouraged the child to go on. 'Yes, my child,' he said gently.

Agnus went on to confess what she believed to be all her sins. The priest gave her a prayer of absolution and made a sign of the cross with his hand to bless the child; he then asked her to say three Our Fathers and three Hail Marys as a penance. Agnus then stood up and left the confessional shakily; as her legs felt like jelly. She stopped in church to say her penance and went outside to wait for Cath before going home.

Easter Sunday was to be the highlight of the two girls' short religious life. They had always watched their parents and other older people go up to the altar to receive Holy Communion from the priest, while they sat in the pews and watched; but now it was their turn to take a full part in the mass. Both girls were attired in white dresses as they went into the Portland Hotel to hear the service. They were seated in the front aisle with the other children who were making their first Holy Communion; then the bell rang and two altar boys dressed in red cassocks entered the room followed by Father Macfaith; who was dressed in vestments that were all white, to celebrate the Resurrection of Christ.

The priest slowly walked to the front of the altar with his back to the congregation and started to say the mass in Latin. The congregation followed the service with their missals, and responded to the prayers, when required, in a parrot-like fashion. In the middle of the service, Father Macfaith gave a sermon in English; on this day he was focusing on the significance of Easter Sunday for the Christian. Then came the most important part of the service, the consecration, when the priest changes bread and wine into the body and blood of Jesus Christ (which is the belief of all practising Catholics). Next the priest took his own Holy Communion and then it was the turn of the congregation.

The children taking their first Holy Communion went up to the altar rail first and knelt in front of the altar. The priest went slowly along the row of his congregation and came to Agnus. He took a small round wafer of bread from the chalice held it in his hand, and said, *'Dominus vobiscum'* (The Lord be with you).

Agnus lifted her head and looked at the small Holy Eucharist and said, *'Et cum spiritu tuo'* (and with thy spirit). The priest placed the bread on the child's tongue and went slowly further along the row of his kneeling congregation.

After standing up, Agnus turned and walked slowly back to her seat with her hands held together in reverence. When the people's Communion was over the priest completed the service and blessed his congregation with the sign of the cross.

A special breakfast was laid on for the children taking their first Holy Communion. They were all presented with a rosary and a certificate to remember their special day. When they got home there were several chocolate Easter eggs for the girls, which were bought by their parents and the older lads.

★

Early in 1928 Joe rented another shop on Welbeck Street dealing in radio parts and hardware at the back of the shop, and selling sweets in the front.

The British Broadcasting Authority, the BBC, was formed in 1922 and became a corporation in 1927. From the late Twenties the radio became very popular.

The story of radios began in 1887 when a German professor, Heinrich Hertz, proved in a scientific experiment that a current (a flow of electrical charges, or particles) could be passed through the air from one apparatus to another without any contact between the two pieces of equipment.

The Italian scientist Marconi was the first person to use a raised aerial, and earth, to connect the transmitter of a wireless message, to the equipment of person who receives the communication.

In 1897, Sir Oliver Lodge discovered that if the wireless circuits sending out the message was tuned to the same frequency – the same number of vibrations as the receiving circuits, then the wireless signal that was received from the message was greatly improved.

In the early 1900s an electric generator provided the energy for the current that transmitted the radio signals (which were at that time in Morse code) and a crystal detector received the messages.

The thermic radio valve, which was a very important part of the early radios, was discovered in 1904 by Professor Fleming. A valve allows a current of electricity to flow through the radio in one controlled direction. It was later improved until speech and musical broadcasts could be received.

From the late Twenties the BBC transmitted the radio programmes that were received by the aerials and relayed to the radios in people's homes. The wireless waves reached the valves of the radio sets, which had a heated filament in the centre when they were turned on. After receiving the transmitted message, the filament then emitted electrons, which produced a current. The electrons were then sucked through the speakers of the radio; and the speakers reproduced the original sound, if the wireless was tuned to the correct station.

The power to generate the valves in a wireless set during the late Twenties and Thirties was provided by an accumulator, which required charging up at regular intervals.

The accumulators that produced the generating power in the first radios were the forerunners of the modern battery. They were composed of a square glass container which was filled with a liquid mixture of sulphuric acid and distilled water. Inside the accumulator were two heavy lead plates with a positive and negative connection on the top. The radio owner normally kept two accumulators. One was in the radio, and the other was placed on charge (in the same way as a car battery is charged today). The slow charging process was carried out by connecting the accumulator to the mains electricity for about a week, and cost about fourpence a time. Accumulators were replaced by the dry battery before the beginning of the Second World War.

Because the valves were heated, air eventually would come out, and they had to be replaced periodically. Normally the more valves that a radio set had the better would be its reception.

Types of radio included: Cossor, Mullard, Phillips, Philco's, Kolster-Brande, Murphy, Dynatron, GEG and His Master's Voice (HMV). The four-valve HMV in the early Thirties would cost around seventeen guineas, or could be bought on hire purchase.

Joe's shop on Welbeck Street charged up accumulators and sold radio valves.

Other items in the hardware shop in the late Twenties included: everything dealing with a coal fire, for example; shovels, fire guards, fire grates, companion sets, buckets, chenille cloths and many other items. Also found in the shop were garden tools (spades, forks, rakes, etc.), brass stair-rods, scales with ounce and pound weights; the weights were placed on a one side of the scale and the produce to be weighed was placed on the other, various kinds of rope, methylated spirits, blowlamps, lead paints, various types of oil, stoves and many other items.

Chapter Twelve

Margaret's Wedding

After the May general election in 1929, Ramsay MacDonald became Prime Minister for the second time when the Labour Party gained the highest number of seats, but not an overall majority, in Parliament. The Liberals once again held the balance of power. There were huge problems for the new Government to face involving unemployment, declining trade and financial insecurity.

The great world depression of the Thirties began in the United States of America in the Autumn of 1929 when shares tumbled on Wall Street. The great stock market crash left many banks and business people bankrupt. The outcome was a decline in trade all over the world, followed by a massive slump. British exports were nearly halved in two years; and by 1933 there was at least three million people who were unemployed and many more were on part-time work.

The country's financial situation got steadily worse. In August 1931 British bankers claimed that the problems were caused by a lack of confidence in the Labour Government – which in later years was proved to be untrue. On the advice of King George V, MacDonald dissolved Parliament and formed a new National Government; however MacDonald remained in the Cabinet as Prime Minister. On 8th September, 1931 an emergency budget cut the wages of teachers, policeman, servicemen and other public employees by fifteen per cent. The unemployment benefit was also reduced, and income tax was raised to five shillings in the pound.

A new Coal Mines Bill in 1930 cut the miners' working hours from eight to seven and a half hours a day (this did not affect the Nottinghamshire colliers who had only worked a seven and a half hour shift since the national strike); and the quota system for the production of coal, which had been voluntary for three years, was made law. The control of the selling price of coal also came into being with the new regulations.

The country came off the gold standard in September 1931, on the advice of the Bank of England. This helped coal exports for a short time; but it did not last.

On the local scene, it was decided in 1928 that no more houses were to be built at the present time in Creswell, because of the state of the coal industry. In 1930 the village colliery only worked for two hundred and two days. In the summer the local mine often only worked for two or three days a week. When Harworth Colliery opened between 1928–31, many of the Creswell miners went to work at the new pit.

The first face conveyor was used in the Creswell mine in 1931. This was part of a new system of shift mining which meant that the coal was undercut by machine on the first shift; then on the second shift the coal was loaded onto the moving conveyor and transported to the haulage system; and finally during the third shift the conveyor was moved to the new face and packing to support the machine was built by the miners.

In 1932, a drift with a one in three gradient was driven upwards from the Top-Hard seam – the only seam that had been worked since the Creswell mine had opened – to a new panel, the High Hazel Seam. This seam in later years was to make Creswell colliery famous in the most disastrous way possible.

The Saul family also went through big changes. Around 1930 Walter went to work in the new mine at Thorne as a deputy. On one of his visits home, Walt told Joe that there was a shortage of shops in the new town. Joe decided to close both of his shops in Creswell (the shop on Elmton Road was taken over and run by his wife's family, the Turners, as a hardware shop), and he set up a new business in Thorne. Bill had got married and had a son, Jeffery. He had a house on Duke Street. The rest of the Saul family went to live in the Model. Agnus left school in 1931 and went into service as a maid for the Chief Constable of Nottingham.

The family moved to 236 Model Village. They lived in a house containing three bedrooms upstairs, and two large rooms downstairs, with a kitchen attached to the house. At the end of the yard were out buildings which included an ash toilet and a coalhouse.

1933 was an important year in the Sauls family history, because on 17th April, Easter Monday, Margaret, at the age of twenty-one, married Arnold Hutton who worked in the local mine. He was thirty-one years old and originated from the village of Mosborough; but he had worked at Creswell colliery for about a year.

The preparations for the wedding began early in January when Mary made the wedding cake. Cath went to Marsdens on Elmton Road to buy the produce for the cake.

Mary had always enjoyed baking and considered it a labour of love. This type of work had given her great satisfaction all through her married life; and this was a special occasion which required a special cake.

Returning home with the shopping, Cath placed the bag full of contents on the kitchen table; she took of her coat and hung it on a hook behind the kitchen door. Cath went to fill the black soot-stained kettle with water to make a cup of tea when she heard her mother's voice. Mary was standing at the table looking at the prices on the grocery list.

'When yer've done that, Cath,' she called, 'go and get the panshion out er the out'ouse; yer also want three more bowls and bring er wooden spoon wi' yer. But before yer use 'em, give 'em a wash, we don't want ter poison all the family at once; we can't afford the money fer the funerals!'

Cath went outside into the outhouse and collected her mother's trusty brown panshion, three bowls and a wooden spoon. She washed the containers; put the large brown ceramic panshion on the hearth to warm, in front of the blazing fire, which was also warming the oven, stuck the wooden spoon inside the panshion to dry and placed the other bowls on the wooden kitchen table.

At that moment the steam began to blow out of the kettle spout. 'Shall I mash the tea first, Mam? I'm as dry as a fish!' Cath shouted to her mother, who had gone into the front room.

'Put the panshion on the 'earth first; we need ter warm it before we put them ingredients in,' Mary called back to her youngest daughter.

'I've already done that, Mam,' said Cath. 'That fire's really hot! If it were summer we'd all be roasted outer the room, the 'eat would be unbearable in 'ere.' Cath took the chenille cloth from the side of the black leaded fireplace; she took the kettle from the centre of the fire, poured the water into the teapot, and covered the teapot with a bright coloured tea cosy.

Returning to the room, Mary and Cath sat down at the table to drink their tea. Mary looked at her daughter and said reflectively, 'It's a strange thing, yer know, but even after all these years, and yer've all grown up, I still think of yer all as babbies! I suppose it ull always be the case.'

'That's all right, Mam,' said Cath, smiling. 'We all think er you and Dad as bein' old!'

Mary gave a playful swing at her daughter with the tea towel. 'All right yer cheeky sod! Come on, let's get on, or we'll be 'ere all day,' she said.

Picking up the three bowls, Mary gave one to Cath, saying, 'Get the cookery book outer the front room drawer and find the page fer fruit cakes. Then weigh the flour out that we need and put it inter the bowl. The scales are under the sink. Then get the spices jar outer the pantry and add what yer want ter the flour then mix 'em tergether. Yer'll want some ground almonds outer the pantry as well.'

In the second bowl, Mary mixed the required dried fruit together. From her years of cooking experience she knew the exact amount of each produce that was needed for the cake mixture without having to weigh the produce. In the third bowl she whipped the eggs and milk for the cake together.

'That's all ready, Mam,' said Cath, returning to the table and passing the bowl to her mother.

Mary looked quizzically at the contents. 'Okay, get the panshion off the 'earth, – it'll 'ave dried and should be warm now – then put the stuff outer the three bowls inter it and mix 'em all together,' she told her daughter.

While Cath mixed the produce Mary took the empty bowls away and washed them, collected a cake tin from the kitchen cupboard, wiped it out, and returned to the kitchen table.

'That's all ready, Mam,' said Cath, pointing her finger at her handy work.

Mary looked at the contents in the panshion. 'That's not mixed properly yet. Put some muscle inter it! It's got ter look more smooth and even then that,' she ordered.

Cath continued with her arm breaking chore. About five minutes later she said, "Ow's that, Mam? Does that look all right now?'

Mary once again inspected the mixture. 'That's better,' she said, 'it looks like it's ready now.' Mary took the mixed produce from the bowl, with the wooden spoon; placed it in the cake tin and put it in the oven, 'That's er good job done the rest ull be easy.'

For about five hours the aroma from the baking cake filled the house. Then Mary took the tin out of the oven and pierced the centre of the cake with a steel knitting-needle; the needle came out of the baked object clearly. Turning her head towards Cath she said, 'That's done anyway; I'm pleased wi' that! If that cake tastes only 'alf as good as it smells it'll be a good 'un.

As the time grew nearer to the big day, John decided that for the first time in his life he would treat himself to a new suit. He went to John Naughton, a gents' clothier who had a shop on Elmton Road across from one of the village schools near the Drill Hall. The Naughtons had been in the village for over twenty years and John believed that he could be trusted.

Although John knew the Naughton family well, he was still slightly apprehensive as he looked through the shop window. Taking courage, he walked into the shop. As John opened the door, the doorbell rang. He slowly closed the door – feeling like a mouse who had taken the cheese off a trap and had escaped – and was looking around the store at the merchandise when the owner came into shop through a heavy large curtain that was covering the inner door.

'Hello there, John!' said the shop owner, and smiled at the ostler. 'It's good to see a happy smiling face this early in the morning. What can I do for you?'

John shuffled his feet as if in some sort of discomfort.

'Margaret,' he began, '– me daughter – is gettin' married at Easter, and I was thinkin' about buyin' a new suit for the ceremony, and wondered if yer'd owt that might be wearable.'

Mr Naughton placed his hands on the counter and asked, 'Do you want a made to measure suit? They cost from about seventy shillings and would take about a month to make. There is a selection of cloths in the book.' The owner pointed to the edge of the counter. 'Or, you can have one that's ready-made,' the shopkeeper said, pointing to a rail near the front door. 'They cost between thirty-nine shillings and sixpence and fifty-seven shillings and sixpence.'

John turned to look at the rail full of suits. 'I'll take er look at what yer've got on the peg first, Mr Naughton; there's maybe somethin' ter fit a little 'un like me,' he said.

The shopkeeper showed the ostler four or five different outfits, and John picked out a grey striped three-piece suit that he seemed to like.

'Go in the back and try it on, John, and let's see what it looks like when you're wearing it. There's a small room just at the side of the door that I keep for that purpose,' suggested Mr Naughton.

John did as requested, and quickly returned to the shop wearing the new suit. Mr Naughton turned to look at his customer. 'It fits you like a glove, John,' he declared. 'If you had that suit made to measure it wouldn't fit any better, and it's the cheapest on the rail at thirty-nine shillings and sixpence. Now all you need is a new shirt, and a pair of boots, then you're set up. You'll look better then the bride,' said the shop owner, laughing.

The ostler also bought a collarless blue striped shirt with two loose collars for 10s 6d; and a pair of black boots for 8s 11d.

Mary made most of her own clothes, but for the special day she treated herself to a brown woollen coat with a fur collar for 39s 11d, and a matching fur hat for two shillings.

The wedding was held at St Mary Magdalene's church in the village. The church was built by the Duke of Portland in 1899 at a cost of five thousand pounds. The church has a chancel, nave and two aisles. A tower with a peal of eight bells was later added to the building in 1927; and an oak reredos (an ornamental screen covering the back of the altar) was erected in 1929. The church is capable of seating up to six hundred people.

For the special day the church was decorated with many Easter flowers, including; red and white roses, white and pink tulips, daffodils, Easter lilies, blue irises white heather and trailing ferns.

Margaret's wedding dress and those of the bridesmaid were made by a miner's wife in the top Model. The bride's dress was made of white lace and georgette. She had an orange blossom coronet and veil that was made of embroidered silk. Her bouquet was composed of white roses. She was given away by her father; and she was attended on her big day by Ellen, who was wearing a blue floral georgette dress with a cap and shoes to match. Ellen carried a bouquet of Easter lilies. Agnus and Cath were the bridesmaids. Their dresses were made from a pink floral georgette, and they were each wearing a pink cap, with stockings and shoes to match.

The service was conducted by the Reverend Charles Smith, and Margaret's wedding was only one of at least seven ceremonies that was performed by the same vicar in Creswell on that warm sunny Easter Monday.

All the Saul family, and many friends were at the service. So too were Arnold's mother and father, Charles and Evelyn Hutton.

The happy couple had many wedding gifts. Joe bought a dinner set, Walt a china tea set with a matching pot, and Bill a chiming clock. The girls bought practical gifts: Ellen a pair of double blankets, Peggy a pair of double white sheets, Agnus two Turkish towels and Cath two pillowcases. John and Mary paid for Margaret's wedding dress and the reception afterwards which was held at home.

After the wedding reception, Margaret and Arnold went on their honeymoon to Scarborough.

★

A regular visitor in Creswell was The Harry Tubby's Funfair. The fair was held on the rec. When the bright, gaily coloured caravans, with brass buckets and jugs hanging on their outside, and – usually – a steam engine bringing up the rear entered the village, they were always followed by a parade of local children.

There were various types of roundabouts including galloping horses, with their gaping mouths and large nostrils, which went up and down on large brass rods that were painted red and white; chair-o-planes and motorbikes were also popular forms on the revolving circular platform.

In the middle of the roundabout was a group of musicians with instruments that included an organ, cymbals, drums and bells, all singing songs like *I'm Forever Blowing Bubbles*.

The roundabouts were rotated by a generator with the power coming from a steam engine.

The gypsy women, often smoking a clay pipe, made rock on an open fire from black treacle and brown sugar in a large black soot-stained pan. When the rock was cooled it was cut into small pieces and sold for a penny a lump.

Side-shows included: roll-a-penny; rifle ranges; coconut shies; different coloured metal horses and riders running round a small metal track (people had to gamble on which one of the horses would win); one-armed bandits; ghost trains; Punch and Judy shows, and Gypsy Lee the fortune-teller.

Another regular visitor to Creswell was Sanger's Circus. Often a man would walk through the village streets on large stilts about a week before the circus arrived, and for a lucky few children free tickets were handed out for the first performance.

There would be a large variety of acts, including a woman standing in front of a large wooden partition; and a man throwing hatchets in her direction. The axes landed in such a way that they always surrounded his female assistant's body, but they never hit her. Another woman entered a large man-sized container – or box – and closed the door. Swords were driven through the container where the woman's body should have been, but when the box was opened the woman had disappeared into thin air. Men went into a lion's cage with whips, and the feline animals performed a variety of tricks. Dogs jumped through hoops; there were elephant and monkey acts; fire-eaters, trapeze artists, and the children's favourite – the clowns.

★

One Saturday morning in the autumn of 1933, John was going down the mine to inspect the ponies. He got to the pit shaft and there was no one around except the banksman (the man who supervises the miners into the shaft on the pit top). The banksman turned round and looked at the ostler. 'Yer might as well ger down, John, there won't be anyone else ter go down yet,' he said.

John entered the shaft. The banksman signalled to the onsetter (the man supervising the shaft at the pit bottom) that the cage was coming down into the mine. The banksman then signalled to the winder that everything was clear, both on the pit top, and at the bottom of the mine. The winder then started to release the metal ropes and allowed the cage to descend into the colliery.

John stood in the steam-driven cage; he was holding on to the handrail as he was moving further into the centre of the earth. All of a sudden, about a hundred yards from the pit top, the lift stopped. It bounced back up the shaft for about two feet then back down again, moving up and down for several minutes, like a rubber ball on a piece of string. The ropes on the shaft had jammed. John fell on the floor but could not move his leg. He kept hearing sounds that he thought were signals from the banksman but he could not move his body to respond to them.

Meanwhile on the pit top, the winder had indicated to the banksman that the rope on the shaft was jammed and it would not move. The manager on the pit top was informed and gave instructions that the safety engineers should be called in from Bolsover.

When the three engineers arrived the winder explained the situation; and that John was trapped in the cage nearly halfway down the pit shaft.

The chief engineer explained to the winder that they would have to go down to the jammed cage in a kibble – a large type of bucket that could carry three men. The winder would have to use the engineer's own winding gear. He explained to the winder that for signals to move the kibble up and down the shaft – when required – would be made by a hitting a blacksmith's hammer on the side of the bucket in a particular way. The instructions were as follows:

> One tap of the hammer on the side of the bucket to stop the kibble.
> Two taps to lower the kibble.
> Three taps to indicate that a man was on board.
> Four taps to raise the kibble towards the surface.

The three engineers entered the kibble, tapped twice on the side of the bucket with the hammer, and the winder lowered the men. The engineers reached the top of the jammed cage and signalled again to stop the bucket. The men got out of the kibble and stood on top of the cage. There was a trapdoor in the roof of the cage; and the chief engineer opened the door to see John's prostrate body lying on the lift floor.

'Are you okay down there, my friend?' asked the engineer, thinking at the same time as he asked the question, what a stupid question to ask.

John looked at the man and gave a whimsical smile, 'I'm okay, but I can't move me leg,' he said.

The engineer entered the cage and examined John. 'It's all right,' he said, 'we will have you out of here in a few minutes.' He shouted to his colleagues who were still standing on the cage. 'I want some splints, bandages and a Lowmoor Jacket.' Turning back to John, he said, 'I think you've smashed the middle of yer femur. It's usually the case in this type of accident.'

'I think yer right,' replied John; 'I've spent the last thirty years doin' first aid on other people and now it's my turn ter be the patient.'

'Your type are usually the worst,' said the engineer, laughing. 'It's like a doctor having an operation; you know too much for your own good!'

When the equipment arrived from the surface, the engineer carried out the first aid using the splints and bandages, and John was taken out of the pit strapped in the Lowmoor Jacket by the kibble. It took nine months for the injury to heal and John was left with one leg two inches shorter then the other, which gave him a limp for the rest of his life.

Chapter Thirteen

Creswell's Cinema

Ramsay MacDonald was replaced as Prime Minister by Stanley Baldwin in May, 1935. Baldwin in turn was replaced by Neville Chamberlain in May 1937. There was around this time much concern among the British people about the prospect of another war.

From 1936 onward there was a steady increase in the demand for coal, mainly because of the Government's rearmament programme. Chamberlain made a bold move to try to avoid the war by having a face-to-face meeting with Adolf Hitler on 15th September, 1938, which proved to be unfruitful.

At home at this time there was still nearly 1,800,000 people unemployed in Great Britain.

In September 1937 the Nottinghamshire miners union again fused into one big union. The dispute between the two factions came to a head because of a major dispute at the Harworth colliery. However, the major reason for the eventual amalgamation, was probably the resurgence of membership in the official union (the national union did not recognise the Spencer Union as an official union) in the Nottinghamshire area, when more miners became employed because of a bigger demand for coal to supply the factories for rearming the British forces.

To improve the safety standards in their mines, the Bolsover company appointed a safety officer – to cover all their mines – in 1935; and they introduced new safety measures, which included protective helmets and gloves for all of their employees.

A fully mechanical endless-rope haulage system had been installed at the Creswell pit; and the colliery baths were opened on 14th January, 1935. However, the mine was still on short-time working because the quota system for coal remained in force until the middle of 1939.

During 1937 the Sauls moved from the Model, to live in a semi-detached bungalow at 1 Portland Avenue. These new bungalows were originally built for injured miners. John was given the first choice of the one-storied homes, because of his senior position at the colliery. In later life, both John and Mary were able to sit for hours and watch the villagers walking up and down Skinner Street from the window in their front room.

Cath had left school and was working at Barringer's metal factory in Mansfield. Agnus had changed her job, and was working at the Ransom Sanatorium for TB suffers. By 1938 Margaret had two sons, Denis and Terry. Joe had bought a plot of land at Bridlington. He built a house and shop there and went to live in the seaside town. After an industrial dispute at Thorne, the mine was closed and Walter took over Joe's old shop in the town.

★

On Thursday 2nd June, 1938, John Saul was working on the night shift. This was unusual for the ostler who normally worked on the morning shift, because that was the time of the day when his presence at the mines was mostly required. However, there were two reasons for him changing his normal shift. Firstly his colleague, the ostler's mate, who normally worked on the night shift, had been taken sick with pneumonia and was unable to come to work. Secondly, the mine had worked out its quota of coal for a required period, and was to be closed down for a week.

John wanted to be sure that the ponies were put into their stalls correctly before their weeks rest. There were only sixteen ponies in Creswell mine now. Their numbers had slowly dwindled because of the introduction of conveyors and mechanical haulage systems for removing the coal (and men) out of the mine.

The man-riding haulage system consisted of two trains, called a paddy, that were attached together by a rope; and was called an endless-rope system; which was motor driven. Normally, when one of the trains was on the coalface the other would be somewhere near the pit bottom; however the ropes were adjustable and could be slackened and tightened as required. The tubs could be fastened to the rope either singly or in sets. The man-carrying tubs usually carried four people, and travelled between two and four miles an hour.

About 12.30 in the middle of the night, John was sitting near the stable eating his snap, when he heard a very large crash and the screaming of men. He stood up and walked down the loader-gate, the gate (or road) leading from the coalface, and was shocked at the sight that he saw in front of him on the road. The paddy had stopped, there were tubs derailed all over the loader-gate; and there were a number of men lying in various positions badly injured across the road.

John rushed to the man who was closest to him. The miner was holding his arm and seemed very dazed. He lifted his head and looked up at the ostler, and said, 'Don't worry about me, John, I'm okay, but there's some men badly injured at the front of the paddy. Go and see ter them first.'

Fighting his way to the head of the derailed train, through overturned tubs and injured men, John managed to reach the front of the paddy. What he saw filled him with horror; three men were laid on the ground, and they were motionless. Out of the corner of his eye he saw a young man about eighteen who was ruefully rubbing his arm. 'Are you okay, son?' asked the ostler.

'Yes, I'm a bit dazed; but other than that I'm all right; it's just shook me up, that's all,' replied the young man.

'Do yer think yer can run ter the pit bottom and get some help, as quickly as possible?' John asked. 'We're goin' ter need a lot er assistance ter sort this lot out. Explain what's 'appened, and that the whole 'aulage system will be blocked with all them derailed tubs.' The man nodded and set off on his way out of the mine heading towards the pit bottom.

John turned to examine the first prostrate man. He felt for his pulse, but there was no response. He opened the miner's shirt to listen for his heartbeat; but there was nothing there. The ostler felt a shiver go through all of his body. He looked into the man's eyes; and it seemed that the miner was glaring into space. He was dead. John closed the collier's eyes and laid the man on his back. 'Rest in peace, son,' said the ostler sadly. He turned to look at the second man who was lying on the ground; but he got a surprise. The prostrate man was being examined by Bill.

"Ello, son! I didn't know that yer was on nights! Mam said yer was on days after yer'd been around on Sunday.'

Bill did not look at his father, but carried on examining the injured man. 'I wasn't supposed ter be, but I had ter go ter the dentist this mornin'; I broke a tooth on a plum stone yesterday, and I did a swap. But I could say the same about you. Why are yer 'ere tonight?' Bill asked.

John stepped over Bill's back, and started to examine the third prostrate man as he continued his discussion. 'That's er long story I'll tell yer later when it's not quite so 'ectic,' he replied. "Ow's the man yer've just examined?'

Bill bent his head, stood up, and in a strained voice with a lump in his throat, he said, "E's dead. That's two up ter now and there could be more ter come with the look er this lot.' He turned his distraught face away from the dead man, and examined another of the injured miners, trying to give as much assistance as possible.

The man whom John examined next had a weak pulse and feeble heartbeat, but he was not conscious. 'At least this one's still alive,' said John, turning to look at Bill, 'but only just; 'e's in a 'ell of a bad way, we'd better get 'im out first.'

The two Sauls and two other first-aiders tried to examine as many of the injured men as possible. About thirty minutes later the young man whom John had sent to the pit bottom came running back with help from many rescue workers who were carrying stretchers and extra first aid equipment. The lad told John that the pit top had been informed, and that doctors and ambulances were on their way to the colliery.

John asked two of the miners who had come to help with the rescue to stretcher out the unconscious, badly injured man first; and then the two dead men.

Because the derailed haulage system had blocked the roadway; the ninety casualties had to be stretchered over two thousand yards before they got to the pit bottom. It took over one and a half hours to get all of the injured men out of the mine. Many were transported to hospital for emergency treatment.

On their way out of the mine, the Sauls enquired as to what had happened to cause the fatal accident. It seemed that the rope that was attached to the paddy had broken loose from the tubs, and the tubs had run out of control because they were going down an incline. When this was realised the three prostrate men whom John and Bill examined first had jumped from the train in an attempt to stop the tubs by derailing them. They were trying to save their colleagues from injury, by an act of unselfish bravery which had cost the miners their lives.

John learnt later that the third badly injured man whom he had treated in the mine had also died in hospital. He had never regained consciousness; and a week after the accident, nine out of the ninety injured miners were still in Chesterfield Hospital.

*

Creswell had a very active Parish Council. Items discussed by the members in March 1938 included the seasonal opening of the village baths on Duke Street during April. These facilities were utilised by many of the villagers, who had their own swimming and polo clubs. Many people from nearby places like Clowne, Whitwell and Langwith also used the Creswell public baths.

Another item discussed by the Parish Council involved the fire service.

During the 1935 County Review Order there were several boundary changes around the Creswell region. The firefighting facilities prior to that time were performed by local parish brigades who had fire hoses situated at various points in the villages.

However after the review the fire service responsibilities were taken over by Clowne Rural District Council (CRDC), in joint co-operation with the Sheffield fire service, who had placed many fire boxes around Creswell and the other nearby villages.

However, in 1938 many of the fire boxes in Creswell were empty; and one of the councillors asked why they were retained in such a useless fashion. A council official explained that when the boundary changes occurred in 1935, the hoses that used to belong to the local parish brigades were altered to conform to the Sheffield fire service's specifications. The hoses were then distributed among the constituent parishes.

The fire boxes in the village were provided by the district surveyor and the chief of the Sheffield fire brigade. A joint board between the CRDC and the fire service was set up to run the fire service. The joint board however, had refused to foot the cost for new hoses for the boxes because they had not authorised their installation. They were put there before the board was set up.

The CRDC had agreed to pay for a small trailer water pump. But they had insufficient finances to pay for the new hoses, to put into the empty fire boxes.

The parish council agreed to write to the CRDC on the matter, believing that the problem of the non-existent hoses was very important, and required urgent attention. However three months later the problem was to become very significant.

★

The local cinema in Creswell, on King's Street, was a popular venue for many of the villagers. The first sound films came into being in 1928. The first colour films developed slowly by various attempts to achieve natural reproductions; but the word, Technicolor, was first applied to film making in 1928. By 1938 films were a very popular form of entertainment. Films seen around the local cinemas that year included: Spencer Tracy in *Captain Courageous*; Chili Bouchier in *Minstrel Boy*; Bob Steel in *Big Calibre*; Kermit Maynard in *Wildcat*; Shirley Temple and Victor McLaglen in *Wee Willie Winkie*; Paul Robeson and Elizabeth Welch in *Big Fella*; Cary Grant in *Souls of the Sea*; Eleanor Powell and Nelson Eddy in *Rosalie*; and many more. However; the Creswell picture house itself was to become a talking point among the villagers for many years to come.

On Friday morning 29th July, 1938, Ellen and Margaret had walked up to Portland Avenue from the Model to visit their mother and have their regular weekly chat. So Mary was not surprised when she heard the voices of her two oldest daughters laughing together when they walked down the side of the bungalow. Mary was at the white oblong pot sink washing the breakfast pots, when Margaret opened the backdoor and nearly fell into the bungalow as she tripped over the doorstep.

'Drunk again!' said Mary, and laughed at her daughter. 'Yer might as well be the noise that you two were makin' comin' up the yard!'

Ellen followed Margaret into the door but ignored her mother's comments; 'I bet yer ain't 'eard the latest news, Mam?' she asked.

'I ain't been outer the 'ouse all mornin' and I've seen no one since late on yesterday. The only things that I spoke to was the birds when I threw them some crusts; so it's not likely that I would 'ave 'eard owt about owt, is it?' Mary replied, and turned back to the sink where she carried on washing the pots. 'Come on then, let's 'ave it. What yer talkin' about?'

Ellen unbuttoned her coat. 'Yer not goin' ter believe this, Mam, but the picture 'ouse was bont down last night. Apparently yer could see the fire fer miles around,' she announced.

Mary stood with her hands on the sink looking at her daughters in disbelief. 'I don't believe it; yer kiddin' me on!' she exclaimed.

'It's true!' said Margaret, laughing. 'It's not really funny I know; but yer still 'ave ter laugh, don't yer? Come on, Mam. Leave them pots; yer can do them later when we've gone. Let's go inter the front room and we can 'ave a chat. There's no rush fer them.'

Mary went into the living room followed by her two girls. She put the kettle on the fire and they all sat down in a semicircle in front of the burning flames until Mary said again, 'Come on then, let's 'ave it! When did it 'appen?'

Ellen rubbed her hands with excitement. 'It seemed ter 'ave 'appened in the early 'ours,' she continued. 'About four o'clock this morning Joe Rogers, the cinema owner, was woken up because 'e could smell smoke. When 'e got up and looked out er the window, all the middle of the Electric Palace was on fire – it was all in flames – and there were large clouds er smoke comin' from the cinema's ventilators. Apparently he ran down ter the telephone kiosk near the post office on the Elmton Road and telephoned the Sheffield fire brigade.'

Mary looked at Ellen in disbelief. 'Go on, what 'appened next? Was anyone 'urt?' she asked.

Ellen continued, 'When 'e got back 'ome 'e got 'is wife and son outer bed and then he went ter wake up Mr Ward, yer know, the cinema manager?' – Mary nodded her head – 'Well, apparently the Ward's 'ouse was full er smoke cause it's attached ter the cinema, yer know. Mr Ward got 'is wife and two kids outer the 'ouse and brought all of 'is furniture out as well. It doesn't seem as though 'e was takin' any chances.

'Whilst 'e was doin' that, young Joe – yer know Joe Rogers's son?' Mary once again nodded her head, still wondering if it was a fairy tale. 'Well 'e got the 'ose that was outside the front er the cinema and started spraying the stage, which seemed ter be the least affected part er the cinema. It was burnin' less then the other parts, I think. But they say it was like pissin' in the wind fer what good 'e was doin'.

'When the fire brigade came – it took em about twenty minutes – they reckon that they didn't need ter be told where the fire was they could see it from Clowne Road.'

'How long did it take em ter get it out?' asked Mary.

'About two 'ours they reckon,' replied Ellen. 'They fortunately managed ter confine it ter the cinema. Mr Ward's 'ouse wasn't touched; at least that's a blessin'. Still 'e'll 'ave ter put all the furniture back inter the 'ouse; and I bet 'e's got some decoratin' ter do. Mind you, they said that the fire brigade got a lot er 'elp from some men in the village who pumped some watter from the stream on Mansfield Road back ter the cinema.'

'It's a strange thing about them village fireman, because they were sayin' in the *Worksop Guardian* the other week that the parish councillors were askin' the CRDC why a lot er them fire boxes in the streets were empty; and there'd be trouble if an accident occurred,' said Mary.

'Well, they might do somert about it now,' said Ellen. 'It looks like it's another case er shuttin' the stable door when the 'oss 'as bolted.'

'But that's not the funny part!' Margaret said, laughing.

Mary looked at her daughter and said with a slight smile on her face, 'Trust you ter turn other people's misfortune into er joke. Come on, let's 'ave it!'

Margaret looked at the other two women with a sheepish grin. 'Well! in the middle er the week Mr Ward put up an advertisement fer a film outside the Palace that should be comin' next week, and yer'll never guess what it was called!' she said.

'I know yer burstin' ter tell us,' said Mary, trying not to laugh at her daughter's antics, 'so get on wi' it.'

Margaret continued, 'I read about the film in the paper last week. It said it's a breathtakin', beautiful and gorgeous musical, which is dramatic and thrilling. It stars Jeanette MacDonald and Warren William; and yer know what it's called?' Margaret waited for the two women to shake their heads, then went on drawing out her words. 'It was called *Firefly* but I think the bleedin' firefly must 'ave come and gone last night, and bont the bleedin' cinema down!'

The three Sauls laughed uncontrollably. After a short while Mary dried the tears from her and said to her daughter, 'Trust you, Margaret, ter see the funny side of it; but ter be serious, was anyone 'urt?'

'Two of the firemen were slightly injured from falling debris, one on the head and the other on the hand; but no one was seriously injured, thank goodness,' replied Ellen.

In 1939 the Rodgers family built a new cinema in Creswell on Elmton Road, next to Brough's grocery shop and it was called 'Regors'.

Chapter Fourteen

The Second World War

On 15th September, 1938, Neville Chamberlain had a face-to-face meeting with Adolf Hitler at Berchtesgaden, hoping to find common ground for discussion between the two countries. But the meeting turned out to be unsuccessful. There were still problems in Britain with nearly 1,800,000 unemployed people unable to find work.

Conscription of young men into the armed forces was introduced in May 1939. This was the first time that conscription had happened during peacetime in the history of the United Kingdom.

On 1st September, 1939 the German army crossed the Polish border. On 3rd September, 1939 Britain and France declared war on Germany for the second time in twenty-five years.

Neville Chamberlain resigned as Prime Minister on 10th May, 1940 and his place was taken by Winston Churchill, then aged sixty-five. A Coalition Government was set up to deal specifically with the problems of the war. Clement Attlee, the Labour leader, was the Deputy Prime Minister.

The Battle of Britain started in August 1940, and London was bombed for seventy-six continuous nights.

The United States of America joined the war in December 1941. At that time F. D. Roosevelt was their President.

Ration books had been issued by the British government in September 1939. However, it was not until March 1940 that the fixed allowance system came into operation. The first produce to be rationed included bacon, sugar and butter. Cheese, jam, marmalade and cooking fats were rationed in March 1941, soap in 1942 and petrol in July 1942, as were sweets, chocolates and various types of clothing and footwear. White flour was limited in the early part of the war but there was an adequate supply of wheatmeal (bread was not rationed until after the war). Cigarettes, spirits, beer, toys and fruit were in very short supply and in many cases they were unobtainable. Queuing for goods during the war was a national pastime for the British housewife.

The Ministry of Food placed regular weekly advertisements in local and national newspapers giving advice to the general public on how to make the best utilisation of the food that was available. Many recipes were concocted, such as the famous Woolton pie (Lord Woolton was the Minister for Food during the war), which included potatoes, parsnips and herbs; and there were many other inventive ideas. However, Woolton did ensure that every child in Britain had adequate daily supplies of orange juice, milk and cod liver oil.

Gas masks were issued to every person in Britain, but they were never required. Probably because Germany was very short of rubber supplies, only a limited number of the German people could have been supplied with suitable masks, and Adolf Hitler might have been concerned about any form of retaliation from enemy forces.

Massive barrage balloons were floated in the air over Britain's major cities in an attempt to disrupt the enemy's low-flying bomber aircraft. Air raid shelters were built in parks, back yards and other positions. On the eve of the war the Government evacuated over a million mothers and children out of the large cities. However the action was not a great success, and many returned to their homes before Christmas in 1939. Iron railings were removed for making ships, and aluminium pans were collected to build aircraft.

Many enemy aircraft flew over Creswell on their way to attack Sheffield and the chemical works at Staveley, as anti-aircraft guns were fired from the Station Hotel yard.

In the Creswell mine, an electric siren was installed early in 1941. This was also the year that the original Top-Hard seam ceased production; and from that time, all coal from the colliery was extracted from the High Hazel seam in three directions.

Just after the outbreak of the war, The Secretary of State for Mines met the miners' union officials to gain support for improved productivity in the collieries. The government believed that thirty to forty million tons more coal would be required for increased production in Britain's factories than in the years before the outbreak of the war.

One major problem in the mining industry was wages. Many people who were working in factories were now earning twice as much as a collier in the mines. Abstenteeism and the ageing population of the miners were also causing concern. During the early part of the war many of the young miners had joined the forces – in the middle of the war forty per cent of miners were over forty and twenty per cent over fifty.

The call-up of miners had occurred early during the war. The major reason was that when France fell to the Germans in 1940, Britain had lost her only major trade exporter. For a time there was an overcapacity of coal in the country, because the coal that would have been exported to France became available to the local market. However within a very short time, demand once again outstripped production.

The conscription of miners was stopped in 1941 – when the damage had been done – after the coal shortage had become very acute. In June 1942, the coal situation had got so bad, that the Government employed a General Coal Controller, who was assisted by Regional Controllers to oversee the mining industry. However the ownership and finances still remained in the hands of the private owners.

During the war many new clubs, associations and services came into existence, and others were strengthened in numbers, in Creswell. They included: a produce club; The Women's Voluntary Service (WVS); Women's Institute; General War Purposes Committee; British Legion; War Savings Committee; and many more groups were set up to assist in the war effort.

During the war in winter months, Creswell's Colliery Institute was utilised for evening classes, which included subjects such as art, needlework and cookery; dressmaking, industrial art, keep-fit, wartime cookery, reading, English and soft furnishing. For youths there were a Scout leadership course, mechanical drawing, map making, and motor engineering.

An important club in the village was the Produce club, which began early in 1941 under the presidency of Dr Samual Evans. There were three sections of the club: a horticultural division; a poultry and rabbit section (known as the fur and feathers club); and the pig club. Members were allowed to breed a pig every three months, but later it was extended to six months.

Over four hundred and twenty villagers were members of the three sections of the club. The committee had been able to obtain over one hundred and fifty extra allotments for their patrons in the horticultural section. They were situated opposite Morven Street, on Skinner Street and Mansfield Road. The club were able to purchase seeds and fertilisers at wholesale prices. In October 1942 they purchased all of the seeds that their members required for the coming spring. For example, they bought eight tons of seed potatoes at an average cost of 1s 9d a stone (the average price in the shops for that year was 2s 2d a stone). They were able to purchase a variety of fertilisers including six tons of lime at two shillings a stone. The club also showed a variety of Ministry of Agriculture and Food films to assist their members to obtain a better crop yield from their seeds; and gain a more efficient and effective animal rearing programme.

John Saul was a member of all three sections of the Produce club. He still had his allotment at the side of the Crags were he had his pig shed; but he also rented an allotment on Skinner Street were he had a chicken shed and some rabbit hutches.

During the war George Vardy (Agnus's husband) was in the army and was away from home for most of the period of the hostilities. Their first son Derek was born in September 1940. For most of the war Agnus lived with her parents in Portland Avenue, and worked as the postmistress in the village. For much of the time Derek was cared for by his grandparents. John enjoyed taking Derek to the allotments. He had a large home-made wooden barrow that was painted green; he would ride Derek to and from the garden in the one-wheeled vehicle.

The animals were always an interest to the child, especially the warm furry rabbits, and he would assist his grandfather with their feeding. As John was now in his sixties, a small child running about his feet seemed to give him as much pleasure as his gardening. It was always one of John's proud boasts that his family never starved because he was able to provide them with food from his gardens, by growing fruit, vegetables, eggs and livestock for nearly all of the year round.

Amongst the entertainment in the village during the war were regular dances organised by the women's section of the British Legion. They were held in the council school. Several bands were available during that period and appeared regularly in Creswell. They included a group of local musicians called the Harrison Band. They played the usual old-time dances, such as the waltz, quickstep, and cha-cha. They also sang the old war-time favourite songs, like *We'll Meet Again*, *The White Cliffs of Dover* and *Till the Boys Come Home*. These dances were always patronised by Cath and Agnus.

A very important form of entertainment during the war was the wireless. Many of the announcers became as well known as film stars. There was the daily cookery programme at 8.15 a.m., called Radio Kitchen, which explained to the listener how to make recipes such as fat free and eggless cakes. There was a daily programme from the radio doctor, Charles Hill. Entertainers in the form of comedians, such as Jack Warner and George Formby and singers like Vera Lynn and Gracie Field could all be heard across the airwaves. When the American forces were stationed in Britain the American Forces Network was obtainable. The British people could listen to comedians like Bob Hope and Jack Benny, and swing music, which was all the rage, from bands like Glenn Miller, Tommy Dorsey and Benny Goodman.

Creswell's own colliery brass band also made several programmes for the BBC radio during the war years, and later during peacetime.

National and daily newspapers were always available – though on occasions they were smaller then pre-war editions. Children's comics and women's magazines could also be purchased on a weekly basis.

Regular whist drives organised by the St John and Red Cross Brigades were held in the senior school at Creswell. The money from these meetings went to the general War Fund. Special prizes were given for the victors of the card games, such as a live pig; and a bunch of grapes as a prize in the raffle could make over two pounds. Mary and John always enjoyed these evenings, especially the refreshments and the banter among the locals at the end of the night.

The Clowne RDC had undertaken to raise money towards a warship at the end of 1941. The adopted boat was called *Britomart*. The target for villagers in Creswell was twenty-two pounds. Bill and William helped to raise money for this fund by taking around the local streets an old gramophone belonging to Joe, and playing records to their neighbours. They made 10s 1d during one day.

The War Purposes committee always provided a Christmas gift for every child in the village during the war years.

There was a salvage campaign in the village, which was only a small part of a nationally organised programme, and was supported by all of the groups in Creswell. There was a designated collector who would gather together all types of metals and old clothing, in every street in the village and deliver it to a designated point in Creswell at the Methodist chapel situated on Mansfield Road.

A darts league that ran through the winter was very popular with many of the miners. There was a billiards league and a domino club. Also in the village during the war years was an adult evacuee club. They met on Tuesdays and Fridays every week in the Drill Hall. They arranged regular Beetle Drives for their members. The tennis club, cricket teams and various football teams were all part of the activities in Creswell during the dark war years.

An important visitor to Creswell at the end of September 1942 was the labour controller for the Notts-Derbyshire mining area, Mr H. Hicken. Mr Hicken was well known by the miners in the village because he had been the union secretary for north-east Derbyshire before the war.

The meeting was held in the Regors Cinema at the request of the village pit production committee, to give the men a chance to find out what problems were occurring nationally in their own industry. John, Bill and William (who was still on the union's committee) were discussing the meeting over a pint in the local club.

'What do yer think 'e was on about when 'e was sayin' that it was important ter apply manpower, machinery and seams more efficiently then they are now. We've only got one seam working these days; and I reckon that we already do what 'e was talkin' about. It just seems like er waste er breath ter me; and I think ter some er the others in the cinema,' John said.

William looked at the pint glass in his hand and replied, 'I would think that what 'e was sayin' was part of a ready made speech that 'e makes every time 'e stands up ter address an audience er miners. 'E knows that our pit is one er the most efficient in the country and that we've been reaching our targets fer weeks. 'E's really just tryin' ter encourage the men ter do their best fer the war effort, that's all.'

'It's a lot er coal stocks less then last year at this time, though, don't yer think so?' asked Bill. 'Thirteen million tons short, I bet they'll never make that up; and anyway they want ter go and look in other places. They reckon our region, the North Midland region, 'as an 'igher output per man then anywhere else in the country.

'What's more I can't understand what 'e means when 'e says that fourteen thousand men 'ad returned ter the pits out er the factories this year, but the output from the mines was about ten thousand tons less then before they came back ter the mines,' Bill concluded.

'It's not impossible when yer think about it,' said John. 'Lots er the young uns 'ave been allowed ter go inter the army; but many of the men they are settin' on terday are over forty and 'aven't been in the mines fer years and it's a 'eavy job. Many of 'em aren't able ter do it any more; in fact when they get tired in the later part er the week they're more of er 'indrance then an 'elp. What's more, most of the miners aren't used ter working six full days er week. Don't forget, the pits, were all on short time before the war. It's like askin' 'em ter do two weeks work in one when yer compare it wi' three years ago.'

'That was a good 'un though!' said Bill. 'The miners got an increase in wages this year of twenty-five per cent, plus a bonus. But after they got the rise there was an increase in absenteeism and output was still declining. It's no wonder that miners 'ave er bad reputation.'

William was still twisting a pint glass in his hand. 'I think they've got a real problem. I wouldn't swap them places fer all the tea in China. But at least there's only three per cent absenteeism in Creswell's pit, and we do meet our targets,' he said.

Under The Essential Works (Coal Mining Industry) Order, 1941, it was illegal for a collier to leave his job; and for his employer to dismiss him without the approval from the National Service Officer, who also had the power to discipline regular absentees who were referred to him by the colliery management. However, labour supply in the mines during the war was, by the middle of 1942, totally inadequate. Ernest Bevin, the Minister of Labour, announced that men who were called up for national service would be given the choice of going into the forces or going down the mine. Although there was some response for the mining option, the numbers required were insufficient and the Government believed by the end of the coal year that the mining industry would not be able to function efficiently because of a shortage of manpower.

Bevin decided in July 1943 that desperate measures were required to solve the shortage of colliers. He announced that for every ten men called up for national service, one would be designated to go into the coal mines. These very reluctant recruits were called 'Bevin Boys'.

Central establishments were set up in each district to train the Bevin Boys; for Nottinghamshire, the place selected for training was Creswell. The boys and men were billeted in small concrete or tin huts at the other side of the iron railway bridge, adjacent to the railway lines that were part of the colliery's pit top.

Before the war, it was normal practice for a boy when he started at a colliery to learn the workings of the pit top, then go down the mine and start at the pit bottom and carefully progress to the coalface; slowly gaining experience in the full workings of the mine. However, with the advent of the war very few, if any, of the mines were offering any form of training or apprenticeships for new employees.

A provisional training scheme for the new mining recruits was introduced in November 1942 under a special branch of The Ministry of Fuel and Power, which included the appointment of specialised mining inspectors; these were to train the Bevin Boys, and the other men who had opted out of the forces to go into the mines.

The specialised inspectors were assisted in their work by the colliery management: the overmen, supervisors who had overall charge of an area in the mine; deputies, who were supervisors just under the overmen; and the shot-firers who drilled holes into the coalface, put charges into the holes, and fired the explosion to release the coal from the coalface.

The major shortage of miners in the latter part of the war was on the coalface. This was where many of the enlisted men were retrained, on jobs such as packers; their job was to pack pockets of dirt an the coalfaces that had been worked out, in order to support the roof of the mine; rippers, who chopped down rough sides of the coalface after the machine (or an explosion) had brought the coal down; cuttermen, who drove the coal-cutting machine; gummers, who repaired old face areas on the roof, floor or ceiling that had broken away; conveyor erectors, who would take down the conveyor on the pit face after a seam had been removed and erect it near to the new coalface; face timbermen, who would set the wood on the face surface; and many more mining jobs.

The first one hundred and thirty-seven Bevin Boys recruits were released from Creswell during February 1944 to work at various mines in the Derbyshire-Nottinghamshire district.

Many of the Bevin Boys were very unwilling miners, and some were prone to absenteeism. The Bevin Boys scheme was supposed to produce fifty thousand miners in 1944, but it only produced fifteen thousand that year, and five thousand nine hundred in 1945. The scheme was abandoned within a year of the war ending.

★

By 7th May, 1945 the German forces had unconditionally surrendered to the Allied commanders.

The following day was VE (Victory in Europe) day. A large street party was held in the Model Village at Creswell. Tables where erected on the village green which was surrounded by the spring flowers in the miners' front gardens that were in full bloom. It was a bright sunny day. Rations were collected from every household in the village, and shopkeepers raided their stores for the special occasion, Union Jacks were hung everywhere; adults wore large red, white and blue rosettes. Children were all off school; many were in fancy dresses and hats. Men were trying to play instruments they had never played before. Desmond Shape, Ellen's oldest son, tried to play the reveille on the bugle – something he had never done in his life. People were singing and dancing in the streets. The excitement was something never seen in the village before.

At night there was a huge bonfire in the middle of the green. Fireworks came out of years of storage in the shops' storerooms. The loud noise of the fire crackers was combined with the colourful sparkles and flames from the hollow cardboard tubes that were filled with gunpowder and/or charcoal. Sodium produced bright yellow colours, strontium the red and copper flames; and barium the delightful blues and greens. The skyrockets, Roman candles and Catherine wheels all lit up the night sky above the village.

The street lights were turned on that night for the first time since the war began: no more putting sticky tape on heavy curtains to stop the light from seeping into the street; no more masking of bicycle lamps to limit their light! For the children who were born in the war, these were happenings that they had never experienced in their lives.

The Saul family menfolk, Charlie Saul, George Vardy and Cyril Duckmenton (Cath's husband) all eventually returned home safely – but not without physical and mental scars to remind them of their experiences – to meet the new challenge of rebuilding a new world from the destructive war; a war that brought a community together in a special way that would never been seen during a time of peace.

However, within five years the villagers of Creswell were to be brought together once again in a catastrophe that would affect, directly or indirectly, every single person living in the community.

Part Five
The Disaster

Chapter Fifteen

The Fire

After the war, in July 1945, the Labour party came to power with a landslide majority of one hundred and fifty-four seats. Clement Attlee became Prime Minister. This was the first time in British history that the Labour Party had ever gained an overall majority of seats in the House of Commons. All of the mines in the United Kingdom were nationalised on 1st January, 1947. The coal output at that time from Creswell colliery was about seven hundred thousand tons per year. Around one and a half thousand people were employed at the mine earning between five pounds and seven pounds a week.

Some rationing was still in force – in many cases the allowances were worse than during the war. Bread was rationed for the first time in July 1946 because of a world-wide shortage of wheat. Milk was rationed to two and a half pints a week at 2d a pint. During the first half of 1947, the country was paralysed by the worst winter since 1880. The only fast-food shop was the chippy. Walking or cycling to work was the norm.

The miners' union was formed into a national unit, the National Union of Mineworkers (NUM) in late 1944. The school-leaving age was raised to fifteen in 1947.

There was a massive house building programme. Rented accommodation was required for men who had been in the forces during the war, and who had returned to the mines. Many young families in Creswell squatted in the old Bevin huts at the side of the colliery to obtain a council house. In 1938 the cost of building the average house was £380; by 1948 it had risen to £1,243.

John Saul retired in 1948 after a trunk conveyor system was installed in the mine, and the ponies were rarely required for physical work. There were only thirteen ponies in the mine at that time. Eleven of them were taken out of the mine and retired into a field at the back of the colliery. Just two remained underground and they were only occasionally used for working purposes.

Bill Saul, William Snape, Arnold Hutton and George Vardy were the only four menfolk belonging to the Saul family who were still working in the Creswell mine after the war.

In Creswell colliery, only the High Hazel seam was in production. The coal was excavated in three directions: the north-west, south-east and south-west districts. About half of the coal was now produced in the latter district.

The pit had two shafts. Down No. 1 shaft ran a five-inch diameter water pipe coming from feeder tanks on the pit top. This pipe supplied water into the mine during the morning and afternoon shifts. However the pipe was turned off for the night shifts to allow the feeder tanks to be refilled from the mains supply. During the night shift the colliery was supplied with water by a pump from the old worked out Top-Hard seam. Coal and men were also transported up and down the mine by this shaft in the Forties and Fifties.

From No. 2 shaft ran a one-inch diameter water pipe; this supplied the liquid to the coal chutes that were situated between the conveyor belts. The water from this pipe was used as a dust suppressant. Stale air, gases and excessive coal dust were removed from the mine by the main extractor fan at the top of No. 2 shaft.

On leaving the cage after coming down the shaft the miners entered the old worked out Top-Hard seam. This district was mined when the pit was first opened.

The High Hazel seam was reached by negotiating an upward slope, with a one in three gradient, for about a hundred and ten yards. The mine had been extensively modernised: it was one of the safest in the country, with an efficient telephone system, ventilation system and adequate firefighting arrangements. By July 1948 all of the mined coal was transported from the working faces to the pit bottom by conveyor belts. The belts were made up of seven layers of rubber and a thick backing. The first powered coal cutter-loader, made by Meco Moore, was installed on 24th September, 1948 in the south-west district.

From the pit bottom there were two major access roads to the south-west district. The first was the main intake road where coal was transported from the mine on conveyors back to the pit bottom. It was called the main intake road because ventilated air was suctioned into the mine from No. 1 shaft and transported round the mine, through this road, with the aid of several devices, including the main extractor fan, air crossings (some of the crossings were explosion-proof), stoppings, doors and auxiliary fans.

The second major road was the mains return. The miners were transported to and from their work on the paddy (or train) by this route. The paddy system consisted of two trains that were joined together by a rope and was called an endless rope system. One train travelled into the mine, as the other went outwards. This road was called the mains return because the stale air was drawn from the colliery through this roadway, and extracted from the mine by the main fan that was situated on the pit top on the upcast (No. 2 shaft).

Coal was mined during the day and afternoon shifts, with most of the maintenance being carried on during the night.

In 1950 on the south-west districts, all but one coalface from which the mineral was extracted laid beyond a steep geological fault, called the Elmton fault, about 2,710 yards from the pit bottom. At this point the rock strata was thrown down over a hundred and ninety yards going into the mine, dipping at a gradient of one in nine on the intake road. On the way back there was an upward slope for about a hundred and ten yards with a one in six gradient on the mains return road.

Both of the main roadways combined at the end of the mine. They were really only one road that started and finished in the pit bottom in a U-shaped formation.

Four coalfaces were in operation between fourteen hundred and nineteen hundred yards beyond the Elmton fault. On three of the panels coal was extracted by using explosives and the miners transferred the coal on to a conveyor belt. A coal cutter was in operation on the last face which put the mineral directly on to the conveyor belt.

Two of the faces were situated on the intake road side of the mine. One was on the U-bend in the round, and the other was round the corner, and joined to the mains return road.

Conveyor belts leading from the faces transported coal to the No. 3 belt (1,060 yards long); this belt ran the coal into a chute. From the chute, the coal was transferred to the No. 2 belt (1,080 yards long); this conveyor straddled either side of the Elmton drift, feeding the coal into another chute; and finally on to No. 1 belt (1,703 yards long), which delivered the product to within ninety yards of the pit bottom. Tubs were then filled with the mineral and taken from the pit. The chutes between the belts, called a transfer points, had a sheet metal canopy with water sprays to assist in suppressing dust as the coal was transferred from one conveyor to another.

★

On the evening of 25th September, 1950, the fitters had been working on the water pump which had broken down in the Top-Hard seam. This pump supplied the High Hazel districts with water during the night shift. But the pump could not be repaired during the shift. The overman was informed, but no one considered it necessary to inform the surface management. Nothing was done to adjust the water supply from the surface tanks.

During the previous week, the railway track on the road leading to one of the coalfaces had been extended by over two miles. This required upgrading the main rail track on the mains return road for the paddy near the bottom of the Elmton Drift. Work was being carried out at this junction on the night shift. A pony was used to assist the men handling the coal tubs at this point.

To allow the paddy to run, one of the trains was detached from the endless-rope system and left at the meetings, a piece of rail track about four hundred yards past the Elmton drift. The other train was allowed to run freely from the pit bottom, to the bottom of the Elmton Drift where the roadway was being repaired. At the end of the shift the second train would have been re-attached and should have collected the men from their workplace.

During the afternoon shift, No. 2 belt was examined as a standard procedure by the maintenance engineer John Brown. There was a groove cut into the belt which penetrated about two-thirds of the thickness into the rubber, and extended around three hundred yards along the belt some six inches from the edge; this was later believed to have been caused by a piece of ironstone that may have been jammed in the chute at the No. 2 transfer point, when the No. 1 belt had been stopped.

'What do yer think should be done about the belt, John?' Joe Fox the afternoon overman had asked his engineer.

'I think we should arrange fer the shift's coal ter go through and then get it stitched up,' the engineer replied, and inclined his head. This was set in operation. Tom Vardy and Fred Smith, the shift fitters, were instructed to go back to the conveyor at the end of the shift, and tack the rubber belt together with pins until it could be replaced.

Joe Fox waited until the end of the shift and informed the night shift overman, Steve Evans, about the problem and the arrangements to repair the belt. However, Steve was informed that the coal from one of the faces had not been transported out of the colliery. He told the two men not to work on the belt until all of the coal had been delivered to the pit bottom. He probably believed that because the belt had been running for a full shift, and no problems had occurred, that it would be safe for it to run until the rest of coal was out of the mine.

'Do yer want us ter wait until the coal's gone and then do the job?' enquired Tom Vardy.

'No, no! It seems ter be runnin' okay at the moment,' replied the overman. 'I'll get the night shift fitters ter do the job when we've got the coal out.'

'Oh well; we might us well go 'ome, then. Goodnight, boss!'

'Goodnight, lads. And thanks for comin' back,' said Steve.

Examination of the belt by the engineer on the night shift around 8.30 p.m. estimated that the groove extended along the belt for well over two hundred yards in length, and the depth of the groove was now over six inches – much deeper then when it was when inspected earlier in the day.

Around 3.10 a.m. on Tuesday, 26th September, 1950, the belt attendant Fred Clark was working between No. 3 and No. 2 conveyor belt. He signalled to his colleague Jack Smith who was working between No. 2 and No. 1 conveyors, and said, 'Jack, telephone the pit bottom and tell 'em that No. 2 belt is torn and 'as a trailing end; and get the fitters ter repair the belt as soon as possible.'

'Okay, Fred,' replied his colleague.

The two men walked towards each other along the belts to find out where the damage had originally occurred. When Fred Clark was about four hundred yards from No. 2 transfer point, he could smell smoke. Then a hundred and fifty yards away, he could see fire coming from the chute: and flames between the chute, and walls of the roadway at the No. 1 to No. 2 transfer point.

It was found at a later date that the possible reason for the fire starting at the top of the chute was by frictional heat, when a piece of torn belt was wedged either on the delivery roller itself, or between the chute and the belt, as the belt passed round the delivery roller.

Jack walked about seventy yards and reached the chute first. 'There's an 'opper full er torn belt in 'ere, Fred,' he shouted to his colleague. 'I'll call the pit bottom and ask fer the electrics ter be cut off and get some help.' But he still allowed No. 1 belt to run.

It was around 3.45 a.m. when Fred reached the fire in the chute. "Ave yer tried the fire extinguishers, Jack?' he asked.

'No, Fred, I can't lift 'em wi' me bad back and leg,' Jack replied. Fred applied a fire extinguisher with no effect, and a second one failed to work.

Jack saw the futility of his mate's efforts and telephoned the pit bottom again. Alan Kirk answered. 'It's me again, Alan,' said Jack, 'this fire in No. 2 chute's worse. Get as much help as yer can and yer'd better get the fire fighters from Chesterfield as quick as poss, and tell the management. Can yer turn off the electric.'

'Okay, Jack. There's some 'elp on its way from the north-west district now,' came Alan's reply.

The overman on the north-west district had telephoned the pit bottom to ask why the power had been turned off. He was informed by the telephone operator about the fire. The overman gave instructions that the manager and under-manager should be informed.

The manager gave instructions that the men should get out of the district as soon as possible, but the overman on the south-west district could not be contacted.

The overman from the north-west district and four firefighters from other areas of the pit travelled on the paddy to the scene of the fire, taking hoses and nozzles which they attached to pipes near the fire. But only a trickle of water came out. They were not to know that the pump on the Top-Hard seam was out of action, and the surface workers had not been informed. So the water supply from the pit surface tanks had not been reconnected. This was the first time in many years that the pump had broken down.

'My gardin' 'ose runs faster then this! There would hardly be enough watter ter watter me misses plants,' said one of the firefighters desperately. Portable fire extinguishers, sand and stone dust were all collected and used effectively. The men believed that the fire was under control – unhappily this was not the case.

Steam from the extinguishers and smoke from the fire had reduced the visibility in the affected part of the mine to nearly nothing. It had masked the fire which was dancing merrily along the main intake roadway, with the assistance of the fan-driven air, which under normal conditions was important for the miners safety; but at this moment in time was assisting the spreading of the flames and noxious gases along the roadway.

Around 5.20 a.m. the trained rescue brigade arrived from Chesterfield, but the water supply was inadequate. They tried several times to get ahead of the fire in an attempt to stop it spreading. However, the heat was too intense, and they failed. The water supply was reconnected to the tanks on the surface after the arrival of the surface engineer on the day shift. By then the fire in No. 2 transfer chute had burnt itself out; unfortunately the fire was quickly spreading farther into the mine.

Once again the firefighters tried to get in front of the fire. However, the wooden props supporting the roof were charred and the lagging round then had burnt away. Some of the steel girders had become twisted by the heat and were badly damaged; and the strata had been greatly effected by both heat and water. The deterioration of the roof and walls made them dangerous, and any further attempt would endanger the firefighters' lives.

The fire had travelled a hundred and twenty-five yards in about ninety minutes. A canary which had been carried by one of the rescue teams showed that it was impossible to believe that anyone could be alive in the working area. Examination of the panel at a later date found that the fire had extended six hundred and ten yards into the mine from the No. 2 transfer point before burning itself out; and the belt had been torn for four hundred and sixty-nine yards.

*

Men working on the district at the time of the fire included the overman, deputies, shot-firemen, packers, face timbermen, rippers, conveyor erectors and various other employees.

Some men were working in coal seams over two miles from the pit bottom. Smoke was observed from around 3.50 a.m. Jack Shaw and Terry Deans were talking together on one of the panels.

'I wonder what's causin' this smoke?' enquired Jack.

'Probably from the cutter machine, Jack,' replied Terry.

At that moment the two men saw two lights coming from a distance up the face. The lights were those from the lamps of the cutter-drivers.

'Where's this smoke comin' from, lads?' asked Terry quizzically.

'It's time ter get out of 'ere, Terry. There's a fire at No. 2 transfer point,' replied one of the men.

'It'll only be a small un,' put in Jack casually. Sadly, there was no major sense of urgency. Some men delayed their departure for a few minutes; others buried their tools for safe keeping; while some men just carried their tools with them. They believed that their mine was one of the safest in the country.

Jack and Terry went to the end of their district. The men took off their knee pads, fastened them round their belts and put their clothes back on in the same way that they would do at the end of any normal shift.

The men had to walk one and a half miles down the main return road to safety; this was the only way they could get out of the mine because the fire was on the main intake road. Their way out was full of dense black poisonous smoke, and they were in total darkness because the mains electricity in the colliery had been turned off. The journey included the tiring upward climb of the Elmton Drift, with a slope of one in six for over one hundred yards, which would take the men's breath away. It was like walking in an oven; their bodies were feeling weak; their chests sore; their eyes red raw, and they were gasping for breath.

Fumes filled the return road blocking out any form of light. On their way out they passed the paddy. The train was stationary, and its headlamps with their thirty-foot beam could not be seen from two yards away because of the dense smoke. In the nightmare, the miners groped and crawled their way along the road, guided only by a rail on the floor, in a moving cloud of black smoke which was so thick that their lamps were useless. All they could smell and taste was the burning rubber. Their walk to safety would last an hour. Men were coughing and choking; at last they arrived at the contact doors which separated them from the smoke and toxic gases, and they were safe.

Unfortunately, of the ninety-nine men who were working on the outside side of the fire, only nineteen men survived the travelling inferno.

The only men who were working on the coalfaces who got out of the fire alive were the men who were employed on the seam attached to the main return road. These men received a smoke warning some ten minutes earlier then the other men, because of the make-up of the ventilation system in the mine.

Of the Saul family, George Vardy and Arnold Hutton were at work that fatal night. Arnold died; but George survived.

★

At around 3.45 a.m. the paddy was travelling out of the pit with face workmen from one of the panels. On the way back there was a power cut. When the power was restored the train was brought to the terminus in the pit bottom. It took the overman and firefighting crew from the north-west district to the scene of the fire, and went back to the pit bottom empty.

There was a telephone call asking for the train to be sent into the district. By this time smoke and fumes had reach the engine house near the end of the return rail. The driver started to take the train into the mine, but he received a message that a pony was travelling on the line. He stopped the train which was at that time a short distance from the stables. During this time a workman on the return road telephoned for the paddy.

About ten minutes later the driver received a signal that the road was clear and started to drive the train into the mine. The train travelled a short distance when electric lighting in the engine house failed; the signalling system was out of action. The power came back on again, but the paddy only travelled seventy yards when the electric signals failed again.

An all-clear signal was received, and the train reached the Elmton Fault. The telephone rang and the driver stopped the train to answer. It was a call from the under-manager asking where the train was going. The driver took the train into the terminus at the bottom of the Elmton Fault. He was overcome by fumes and went to an air terminus to get some fresh air. During this period some men arrived at the Fault and boarded the train – several men were later found dead sitting on the train.

The only way of escape for the men was by the return airway, because the fire was on the main intake road before the Elmton Fault. When the men wanted to get out of the district quickly, the paddy return was not running normally; and it cost the lives of some of the miners, who could not know that one of the trains was detached from the rail system.

A decision to stop the rescue work was sadly made by all parties involved. It was important to stop this very dangerous fire from spreading, and to avoid explosions from the production of firedamp (methane gas). The district was sealed off. Out of a hundred and thirty-three men who were working on the district on the night shift, eighty died; however, only forty-seven bodies were recovered that day.

Two seals one thousand yards from the pit bottom were put into place – one on each roadway. They were built of sandbags into which were placed steel sampling tubs and ventilation pipes. The work was finalised with the erection of a three-foot-thick wall.

The panel was reopened during the Easter holidays in March 1951. The district was cleared to the bottom of

Elmton Fault. At this point there had been heavy rock falls in the roadway. The air pressure was very low, making the ventilation inadequate and unable to cope with the conditions. It was decided to seal the district again at the bottom of the Elmton Fault. By then, however, twenty-seven more bodies had been recovered.

The road was repaired and ventilation restored. The district was reopened on 10th August, 1951, when the last six bodies were recovered.

Chapter Sixteen

The Aftermath

In the early hours of Tuesday 26th September, 1950, news of the fire spread quickly through the village. Mothers, wives, brothers, sisters and children stood silently waiting at the pithead for information of their loved ones; it was a cold windy night with intermittent rain. The Salvation Army and various women's organisations from the village provided the anxious relatives with cups of tea.

Many ambulances were stood waiting, but not one would be used. Rescue teams arrived from all parts of the coalfield, from nearby villages and from Chesterfield fourteen miles away. Many lorries delivered sand which was filled into bags by volunteers. Men were selected to assist the rescue teams underground. George Vardy went back down the mine to assist the rescue workers. His army training and war experience would have been of great assistance. Several wives were not aware of the accident; they were at home cooking their husbands' breakfast.

A message came from the manager which explained how serious the fire was, stating that any hope of rescue for many of the men ahead of the fire was small. One of the rescue volunteers who returned to the surface said, 'The fumes have not only filled the return airway, but they have filled the whole pit as well. Visibility is reduced to a few feet, by dense black poisonous fumes. The fumes are so dense that they are penetrating the breathing apparatus.'

The night and morning went steadily on in a deadly silence and an uneasy peace. Anglican, Roman Catholic and Nonconformist ministers prayed for the trapped men and comforted the worried relatives. The pit top gave no indication of the raging inferno running through the mine over four hundred yards below ground level, until a message came to say that all hope had gone.

The final statement said:

> We regret to announce that at 4 a.m. a fire occurred underground at the No. 2 transfer point on the main trunk conveyor at Creswell Colliery. The fumes from the fire circulated rapidly through the mine. Eighty men working beyond the fire were unable to get out. Rescue teams were rapidly on the job. But in spite of their efforts, it was not possible to rescue any of the trapped men. All possible steps were taken to combat the fire but it was impossible to prevent it from spreading. After a full inspection underground with workmens' representatives, the management and HM Inspectors of Mines, it was the unanimous opinion that any attempt to recover more bodies was bound to fail; and such an attempt would inevitably involve further loss of life. It was unanimously decided that no other course remained except to seal off the affected part of the pit. This work is now taking place.

★

All was quiet on the pit top except for one small incident: a young widow collapsed into the arms of a priest and a policeman. A cameraman photographed her, and his camera was pulled from his arm and crushed by the boot of a miner. Not a word was said.

Only a week before the disaster a newsreel was shown about the disaster at Knockshinock in Russia. Could this have been a premonition? In 1939 the first picture house in the village showed a poster of the coming *Firefly*. A few days later the cinema was burnt down.

There was not a child at school in Creswell who had not lost a relative. One miner would have been at work that night but was on holiday; he lost three brothers – all the men were married. Two of the Saul sisters stood together in the crowd. Both their husbands were at work that night – one had died, the other was saved. The Saul parents stood behind their daughters unable to say a word. They had only memories of a sunny wedding day seventeen years earlier, and the happy times since. Now they faced the loss of a son-in-law with two sons and a two-year-old daughter.

A wife of just one month was at home cooking her husband's breakfast, when her mother knocked on the door to tell her the sad news that she was now a widow. For one woman it was exactly seventeen years earlier that she had lost her first husband in a mining accident at Creswell. That night she was a widow in the same way for the second time in her life. One woman returned home on the Tuesday morning from Chesterfield, after the funeral of her mother, only to be told that her husband had died in the fire.

That night at the pithead a service was held. The villagers sang *Abide With Me*. Chapter twenty-one from the Book of Revelations was read: 'And God shall wipe away all tears from their eyes, and there shall be no more death, neither sorrow, nor crying, neither shall there be any more pain; for the former things are passed away.'

Over two thousand people were gathered together in the pit yard that Tuesday. During the night forty-seven bodies were recovered. Twenty men were found sat together waiting for the train. Men were still suffering under the strain of many hours of work at appointed tasks: mechanics, surface men, rescue workers, timekeepers and scientists patiently dealing with air samples. Volunteers from the whole community and many of the villagers close by came forward to do what they could. Just a few yards away the picturesque cricket ground, football field and bowling greens were sunk into oblivion during the darkest hours of the villager's history.

On Tuesday morning, the dead miners were brought to the surface. The cause of death: carbon monoxide poisoning. A temporary mortuary was set up in the miners' Institute in the Model. Where even the stage had to be used to lay the dead miners out; in order that they could be identified by their families.

The village was stunned into silence. For nine days no coal was turned in the mine. Not even the sounds from the pit could be heard. No shunting of trains along the railway line; no clanking and clashing of the rail wagons; no rattling of tubs; no vibrating machinery; no echoes of the wheels on the shaft's pulleys – nothing could be heard but the singing and lamenting cries of birds circling around the village; and the calling of the wind as it blew in the stillness of time. There were no noises of children playing on the roads; no groups of wives and husbands to be seen gossiping in the streets – even the dogs and the cats seemed to have disappeared. Everyone was conscious that someone was mourning. For over two weeks no one spoke as they passed each other in the street. The village was so quiet that even the sound of a shop bell could be heard when walking down Elmton Road.

On the Wednesday a sign was placed outside the mine to say that the seals were complete, and the mine would be closed for forty-eight hours.

At a meeting in the Regors, the local picture house was full to capacity, with men standing in the aisles. It was agreed to transfer some of the miners to Bolsover Colliery – two hundred and seventy-eight worked for a short time at Bolsover and work should be started as soon as possible on the unaffected part of the mine at Creswell. This occurred nine days after the accident. The transferred men would be allowed to return to their own employment as soon as possible. It was resolved that none of the bereaved families should ever be in need.

The following Thursday, miners met at the local cemetery in a thirty hour vigil, to dig the graves of their mates. Food and drinks were provided by the women who worked in the miners' canteen, and delivered by the local children.

On Saturday every shop in the village was closed. Every curtain in every street in the village was drawn together. There was a continuous flow of funeral processions. One cortege solemnly left the rear, and another entered the front, following each other from every church and chapel in Creswell. As the sad parade went through the village, all finally heading for one destination, the weather captured the mood of the village; it rained all day. No one spoke a word. They could not; everyone was too full up. That night the graves in the cemetery were covered by a blanket of flowers for the men who had worked all their lives in a deep grave over four hundred feet below the surface of the earth.

Thousands of letters of sympathy and contributions were sent to the various relief funds that had been set up in the village. Offers of help came flooding in from all over the country. The day after the disaster a red Rolls-Royce pulled up in Creswell's pit yard; the driver handed over a cheque for five hundred pounds to the miners' union secretary, from the employees at the Rolls-Royce factory in Derby. There was only one request; the money must be used for immediate relief of the stricken families.

A small village in Shropshire celebrated their harvest festival only two days earlier; they sent all their produce to the devastated village. Old age pensioners sent half a crown and five shilling postal orders; children sent their sweet money – these were gifts of real sacrifice.

An hostel on the South Devon coast offered a free fortnight's holiday to the miners' widows and their families. Many other offers of free holidays came from various holiday resorts around the country. The colliery brass band played on the Leeds United football ground for the relief funds and collected two hundred and thirty-five pounds. Large amounts of money were collected from all over the country by the Wilfred Pickles radio appeal.

For weeks (and years) the men, women and children of the village fought to build their lives. It's difficult to lose a father, a brother, a brother-in-law or a son; to wait for footsteps coming down the yard that you will never hear again; to look at the door and hope it will open in the usual way – but you know it never will; to listen to the idle chatter around the house during a meal time – but all you hear is silence. How do you explain to a family dog, who pines for his master as he looks at a pair of empty slippers at the side of the fire as he waits for his daily walk? You see your sister or neighbour's wife who has lost a loved one, and ask yourself – should I speak? What should I say? What do you say to a widow with seven children – *is coal worth the price that you pay?* How do you mend a broken heart?

> When other helpers fail to comfort me
> Through dark, through light, dear Lord,
> Abide with me.

It's hard to lose a mate you've worked with for years. You've travelled with him daily down the shaft into the mine; walked with him into the district where you worked; discussing things that you both had in common. Then coming out of the mine at the end of the shift together, just glad of the companionship, to sing in the shower with all the other men. A pot of tea in the pit canteen and your first fag after eight hours underground – just to look out of the canteen widow and see the lush grass of the cricket field brings relief to a man's tired eyes and fatigued body. All of a sudden he's gone – God has called him – only memories of his face are left; his voice and his stupid jokes that you both laughed at together. Now, all that's left is a sense of sorrow; a hope that he is at peace, and that one day you will be together again to enjoy each other's company.

In the village of Elmton, just a mile from the mine, stand two large elm trees. A few weeks before the disaster one of the trees was struck by lightning and a large branch was split off. But the tree roots were strong and deep; and with time they had the strength to repair the damage. And so too the community of this very close village gained the strength and courage to rebuild their lives after the tragedy that shook their whole existence. But, like the tree, the people who were there would always have the scars as a reminder, when in quiet moments of thought the memory would return that on 26th September 1950, eighty men lost their lives in one of the safest mines in the country; which is all part of the price that you pay for coal.

September 1998 (Last)

John continued quietly, 'After the fire the people in the village slowly rebuilt their lives. The miners 'ave had their ups and downs, since that time. They won a large victory over the Coal Board in 1972, but they lost the major battle in 1984, which is probably one of the reasons for the state er the place terday.' John waved his hand to cover the whole area where the mine and pit top stood. 'But who cares? And no one will even remember that it existed in twenty years' time, and that all the lives in the village were dependent on that area where the mine once stood.'

The two lads' heads were bowed low, and they were nearly in tears. All of a sudden everything had gone deathly still. One of the lads looked up but John had gone. He looked into the sky in shock and told his friend, 'He's up there, see!'

They both looked up and there was John and the pony floating away. One of the boys looked at the ground where John had been sitting and there was a neatly folded piece of paper. The boy picked the paper up and found that it had writing on; so he started to read the note, which read:

We were on this earth to dig for coal
The mine with its dust were all in our soul
Our families were together for life, people say,
Now it's all gone, it's sad in a way.

The coal in the mine was both good and bad:
It gave us a living, for that we were glad;
But many a man with his life had to pay
For the energy the country used in our day.

The mine is now gone, the coal is all burned
The pit shafts at Creswell are no longer turned;
The power of the future comes from gas, waves and wind –
But what of the families with no wages to spend?

We had our good times, we had our bad
Our work was all hard; and for friends we were glad.
That time is now history and everyone forgets
How coal mines like Creswell brought happiness and sadness,
But never regrets.

The disastrous fire that happen so quick
Left pains in the heart, and made us feel sick;
Out of sadness new strength is gained at a cost
But memories of loved ones will never be lost.

What of the future for our families and friends?
Will the pride of our village dissolve in the winds?
We worked all our lives for a better tomorrow,
But to see it all now brings nothing but sorrow.

The two lads waved at the ostler as he floated away. One of the lads called out, 'We will remember, John,' – *We Will Remember.*